Operation Timothy *Signature* 2

Life FOUNDATIONS

CHRISTIAN BUSINESS MENS CONNECTION

Table of Contents

Life FOUNDATIONS

chapter 1

NEW LIFE IN CHRIST

That's What They Say

"Someone asked whether I ever worried about slipping through the Lord's fingers. I replied that it was impossible; you see, I am one of the fingers. By the new birth we become a part of the spiritual body of Christ."
Donald Grey Barnhouse, pastor

"The world is a great sculptor's shop. We are the statues, and there is a rumor going round the shop that some of us are some day going to come to life." *C.S. Lewis, professor and author*

"Becoming a Christian is not a matter of external physical attachment to a social organization called a "church." Nor is becoming a Christian effected by mental assent to historical or theological tenets of belief. Behavior modification and ritualistic repetition are not the essence of becoming a Christian. Becoming a Christian is a spiritual reality that transpires in the spiritual core of our being."
James Fowler, pastor

When we come to place our faith in Christ, we too find the treasure of a lifetime. Suddenly, our lives are changed, yet we often treat it like a pile of rusty antiques—an interesting find, a momentary lift, and then off it goes to a musty basement in a museum. Like an ancient treasure map, the Bible shows us where to find the true riches we have received through salvation in Christ.

Buried Treasure

Mel Fisher dedicated the prime of his life to finding the sunken treasure of the Atocha, which went down in 1622. For 20 years, he searched and dreamed. He battled bill collectors, the Supreme Court, and the doubt of everyone. The lowest point came when his son, fellow treasure hunter Dirk, was killed looking for the wreck. But in 1985, Fisher found the mother lode: $450 million in ancient gold, silver, and precious gems, 47 troy tons of treasure in all.

The Big Picture

  I. Made that Way

  II. The Source of Eternal Life

  III. Gaining Eternal Life

  IV. Believe, Confess, and Repent

  V. I'm So Sure

"The spiritual life is the life of Christ reproduced in the life of the believer by the power of the Holy Spirit in obedient response to the Word of God."

Howard Hendricks,
professor and author

I. MADE THAT WAY

It seemed like a good idea at the time. Farmers wanted to sell tobacco, and smokers seemed to get pleasure from lighting up cigarettes. Many claimed to experience health benefits like sharper mental acuity and natural weight loss. One ad touted, "Each puff is as cool and refreshing as a frosty drink after a dusty 20-mile hike." That's how tobacco became a multi-billion dollar industry.

But as it turns out, the human body doesn't exactly thrive under constant exposure to smoke. In fact, it's deadly. Instead, our bodies benefit from things like that 20-mile hike. It's how we're made.

Physically, we need fresh air, and spiritually, we were made to thrive when connected to God's Spirit. Other approaches may seem good at the time. But they can sometimes do more harm than good. Salvation is God's act of saving us from choices that once seemed like a good idea, but have resulted in our spiritual destruction.

In what ways were you made to need Christ? Explain.

_____

_____

_____

_____

What other methods have you tried in order to experience wholeness?

_____

_____

_____

Getting Started

In *Life Questions*, the Scripture references and verses were printed in the lesson. Beginning with *Life Foundations*, you will need your own Bible to look up the references. The questions are based on the New International Version (NIV) translation of the Bible. Also, as a part of each lesson, you will memorize a Scripture passage.

Read Genesis 1:26. What do you think it means to be made in God's image?

_____

_____

_____

_____

What happens in Genesis 3:1-13? Name several things that die in this story. In light of these events, why is salvation an important concept?

_____

_____

_____

_____

Spiritually, we were made to thrive

when connected to God's Spirit.

From the moment you were created, you have been a spiritual being. That's true of everyone. Because of this unique design, we function best when the Spirit of God is within us. God specifically engineered us for a relationship with Him. And deep inside, we know it. This aspect of our existence makes us different from every other creature in the world.

IN WHAT AREAS OF YOUR LIFE DO YOU MOST FEEL THE NEED FOR GOD? HOW DOES A PERSONAL RELATIONSHIP WITH HIM ENRICH YOUR LIFE?

_____

_____

_____

_____

_____

WHAT HAPPENS IF WE FAIL TO REALIZE THAT WE WERE CREATED WITH A SPIRITUAL NATURE?

_____

_____

_____

_____

_____

WHAT ARE SOME DIFFERENT WAYS PEOPLE REFLECT THEIR SPIRITUAL NATURE AND THE NEED FOR RELATIONSHIP WITH GOD? WHAT ARE SOME WAYS THEY STRUGGLE TO REFLECT IT?

_____

_____

_____

_____

_____

II. The Source of Eternal Life

Spring of Water

Bottled water is big business, and the most important feature consumers look for in their water is authenticity. They want to know it's fresh from the source. That's why bottlers budget millions each year to carefully craft their brands to give a convincing message of purity.

WHY ARE CONSUMERS SO INTERESTED IN THE SOURCE OF WHAT THEY EAT AND DRINK?

_____

_____

_____

WHEN IT COMES TO LIFE AND FULFILLMENT, HOW IMPORTANT IS IT TO CONSIDER THE "SOURCE" OF LIFE? WHAT ARE SOME SOURCES PEOPLE TURN TO FOR LIFE?

_____

_____

_____

_____

IN JOHN 4:13-15, JESUS SPEAKS TO THE WOMAN AT THE WELL. IN THEIR CONVERSATION, HE DRAWS A PARALLEL BETWEEN A SPRING AND ETERNAL LIFE. HOW WOULD YOU DESCRIBE THAT CONNECTION?

_____

_____

_____

READ THESE PASSAGES FROM JOHN. WHAT IS JESUS SAYING ABOUT HIMSELF AND ETERNAL LIFE?

> JOHN 1:4

_____

> JOHN 6:40

_____

> JOHN 10:10
_____

IN YOUR OWN WORDS, WHAT IS ETERNAL LIFE?
_____
_____
_____
_____

Jesus answered, "Everyone who drinks this water will be thirsty again, but whoever drinks the water I give him will never thirst. Indeed, the water I give him will become in him a spring of water welling up to eternal life." *John 4:13-15*

Making the First Move

Everyone who turns to God has a unique story to tell about it. Some begin the connection in childhood. Others discover it as an adult. And some sense it all along, only to see it come alive during a particular season of life. In each case, God plays the role of initiator. Throughout our lives, He is at work behind the scenes, carefully orchestrating the moments when we come face to face with His reality and choose to pursue the connection on purpose. However you first experienced God, it all began when God reached out through Christ.

ACCORDING TO I PETER 3:18, WHAT IS GOD'S STRATEGY FOR ARRANGING OUR CONNECTION?
_____
_____
_____

EXAMINE JOHN 17:3. JESUS CLAIMS THAT HE IS THE SOURCE OF ETERNAL LIFE. WHAT DO YOU THINK KNOWING HIM LOOKS LIKE?
_____
_____
_____
_____

III. Gaining Eternal Life

Receiving the Gift

We were made to need God, and he initiated the connection. So what now? How do we resolve the tension we feel apart from him? What is required to sign on with him once and for all? Many religious approaches seem to emphasize a variety of tasks that need to be accomplished in order to fully qualify or to justify our worthiness with God. But Jesus' closest followers emphasized the simplicity and availability of connecting with Christ. They describe it more like an undeserving person opening an unexpected gift.

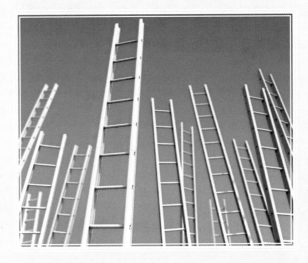

READ JOHN 1:12. HOW IS CONNECTING WITH CHRIST LIKE RECEIVING A GIFT UNDESERVED?

_____

_____

_____

_____

HOW HAVE YOU EXPERIENCED GOD INITIATING A CONNECTION WITH YOU?

_____

_____

_____

_____

HOW HAVE YOU RESPONDED?

_____

_____

_____

_____

IV. Believe, Confess, and Repent

Salvation is a word we use to describe the process of forming a connection with God through Christ. But in the original language of the Bible, there are three other words that give us an important outline of what it means to place your faith in Christ:

> **Pisteuo** – to believe; to be convinced of a matter; to place confidence in a belief to the point of relying on it.

> **Homologeo** – to confess; to agree with; to concede; to declare or profess openly.

> **Metanoia** – to repent; to change one's mind; to retract a previous statement and replace it with a new one.

WHAT ROLE HAVE EACH OF THE WORDS ABOVE PLAYED IN YOUR OWN EXPERIENCE WITH GOD?

> PISTEUO:

_____

> HOMOLOGEO:

_____

> METANOIA:

_____

READ ROMANS 10:9,10. IN THIS PASSAGE, WHAT TWO ACTIONS ARE ASSOCIATED WITH BEING SAVED?

_____

_____

_____

_____

_____

_____

_____

_____

READ ACTS 26:20. IS THE WRITER DESCRIBING CONDITIONS THAT MUST BE MET IN ORDER TO BE ACCEPTABLE TO GOD OR A NATURAL RESPONSE TO ENCOUNTERING GOD? EXPLAIN.

_____

_____

_____

_____

V. I'M SO SURE

For some people, connecting with Christ can be an emotional experience. For others, it's more of a logical, practical step in life. It all depends on your personality. In either case, the experience is valid and real. As a unique creation of God, you are entitled to your own, unique response to His presence in your life.

To become a Christian is to accept an invitation. Whether we laugh or cry or feel a quiet joy when we grasp that invitation, God causes a profound change in our eternal destiny. Our emotions are merely the icing, not the cake. God's work in our lives, based on our assent to His plan, is the substance.

It's normal for Christians to have questions about their salvation. How can we know for sure about eternity? John, who knew Jesus, tells us the facts.

READ I JOHN 5:11-13. IN VERSES 11-12, WHAT EVIDENCE DO WE HAVE OF ETERNAL LIFE?

_____

_____

_____

_____

ACCORDING TO JOHN 10:25-30, WHO HAS THE POWER TO GIVE ETERNAL LIFE, AND WHERE DOES ETERNAL LIFE COME FROM?

_____

_____

_____

_____

WHAT GUARANTEE DOES JESUS GIVE IN JOHN 10:28, 29?

_____

_____

_____

_____

WHAT COMES TO YOUR MIND WHEN THE TERM "ETERNAL LIFE" IS USED?

_____

_____

_____

_____

_____

Hooked on a Feeling

What happens when we accept Christ into our lives? How does it feel? Are there fireworks? These are natural questions. The answer simply depends on you. Have you ever signed a contract of huge significance, such as the mortgage on your first house? Have you ever signed a marriage license? These events shape your destiny in ways you never fully comprehend at the time. They are also acts of the will, which may or may not include strong emotions. Whether you sign them casually or seriously, the contracts are binding either way.

Don't worry: If you don't see fireworks, you're not missing the show!

Here Today, God's Tomorrow

It's the best kept secret around: Eternal life means "benefits" which begin right now. We face an eternity of joy, peace, and perfection; yet, because "to live is Christ," there is hope, fulfillment and abundant living available for this very moment. All in all, not a bad deal!

SUMMARIZE WHAT YOU LEARNED IN THIS LESSON ABOUT ETERNAL LIFE AND ITS SIGNIFICANCE TO YOU.

_____

_____

_____

_____

_____

_____

_____

Scripture Memory Verse: New Life in Christ

I John 5:11-13

> "And this is the testimony: God has given us eternal life, and this life is in his Son. He who has the Son has life; he who does not have the Son of God does not have life. I write these things to you who believe in the name of the Son of God so that you may know that you have eternal life."

Why Memorize and Meditate on Scripture?

When Jesus was tempted by Satan in the wilderness (Matthew 4:1-11), three times Jesus replied: "It is written." Jesus then quoted particular and pertinent Scripture from the Old Testament to combat Satan's attack. In this passage, we see that Satan quotes Scripture in a distorted way to tempt Jesus. Jesus used the appropriate Scripture to refute Satan and show his error. Matthew 4:11 states that Satan then left Christ.

If Christ found the Scriptures necessary to battle Satan, how much more do we need this weapon for our lives? This week you will start hiding God's Word in your heart. Psalms 119:11 says "I have hidden your word in my heart that I might not sin against you." God's Word strengthens and encourages us in the daily battles of life. In addition, it serves as a preventative measure to keep you from sinning against God. Key verses have been chosen to help you grow in your spiritual walk with the Lord. Work diligently to learn them. You are joining thousands of others who have found this the key to their spiritual growth.

How To Memorize Scripture Effectively

Tear out the card in the back of this book on which I John 5:11-13 is printed. You may choose to memorize either the NIV (New International Version) or the NASB (New American Standard Bible). Read it several times, silently and aloud, to get an overall view of the content. Then, begin memorizing the verses, one phrase at a time. Each time you say the verse or a part of the verse, begin by repeating the reference: "I John 5:11-13." Also, say the reference after each time you repeat the verse or part of the verse. It will help guard you against the day when you start saying, "Somewhere, the Bible says…"? Repeating the reference every time fixes its location in your memory.

God urges his people many times throughout Scripture to meditate on His Word and promises to bless them as a result. Once you have memorized the whole passage, begin to meditate on it. One way to do this is to repeat the verse, emphasizing a different word each time. Personalizing the verse often brings added insight and help: substitute personal pronouns into the verse, "me," "I," or your name. For instance I John 5:11-13, personalized, would be:

> "And this is the testimony: God has given me, _____, eternal life, and this life is in his Son. If I have the Son I have life; if I do not have the Son of God I do not have life. These things were written to me, _____, who believes in the name of the Son of God so that I may know that I have eternal life."

Caution: Make sure you know the verse word for word as it is written before you try to personalize it or else you might get confused!

Review is the key to mastering and retaining these verses. So, every day, review I John 5:11-13. Next week, when you begin another verse, keep reviewing I John 5:11-13 daily while you are working on the new verse. The cards are small so they are conveniently portable or they can be taped on your mirror for frequent review! As you encounter various situations and temptations during the week, you will be surprised to see how often God will bring these verses to mind to strengthen and sustain you.

The intent of this memory work is not that of duty or performance but that of growing deeper in relationship with the Lord and your "Paul," as you work on these verses together.

Listen

Audio message for *Life Foundations*, Chapter 1, at www.operationtimothy.com or scan the QR code.

Audio 1

Audio 2

Additional Resources

> *The Pursuit of God*, A. W. Tozer

> *Incomparable Christ, The Person and Work of Jesus Christ*, J. Oswald Chambers

NOTES

[OPTIONAL APPLICATION]

THINK: How could eternal life be available and yet many people won't accept it?

_____

_____

_____

_____

OBSERVE: Choose one of the iconic Indiana Jones movies to watch. Note the passion with which Jones seeks the treasure, whatever it is. Is the goal worth the relentless pursuit?

_____

_____

_____

CONSIDER: A familiar worship song begins, "Lord, you are more precious than silver. Lord, you are more costly than gold…" Now, complete the phrase in your own heart: _"Lord, you are more precious, more costly than…"_

_____

_____

_____

_____

List the "treasures" in your life.

_____

_____

_____

_____

NOTES

OUR NEW IDENTITY

That's What They Say

"First say to yourself what you would be; and then do what you have to do." *Epictetus, Greek philosopher*

"Tell me whom you love and I will tell you who you are." *Arsène Houssaye, French novelist*

"I have had more trouble with myself than with any other man I've met." *Dwight Moody, pastor and evangelist*

"I know this now. Every man gives his life for what he believes. Every woman gives her life for what she believes. Sometimes people believe in little or nothing yet they give their lives to that little or nothing. One life is all we have and we live it as we believe in living it. And then it is gone. But to sacrifice what you are and live without belief, that's more terrible than dying." *Joan of Arc, 15th century national heroine of France*

Define Self

It's a daunting task that sends most of us to the philosophy textbooks or the deep recesses of our own thoughts. *Who am I?* is a question that gives birth to other questions: What measures identity? Success? Appearance? Personal history? Background? Who says who I am? Do I get to define myself? In our complicated, educated culture, the idea of "self" can seem like a hazy thought at best, or, at worst, a hopeless conundrum.

Not so in every culture. In many tribal villages in Papua New Guinea, people and items are identified by one factor alone: ownership. And

ownership is determined by creation. In other words, if you made a paddle, that paddle is yours. More than its function or appearance, the paddle's primary definition is: *yours*. That's why many Christians in these villages refer to God as "Papa/Owner." As Creator, God is the owner of all and, thereby, the ultimate definition of all.

If I am defined by the One who made me and owns me, it makes sense to look back to Him for clues about who I am. It is much more important to know who God says I am than for me to define who I am. Knowing who we are before attempting to live life by doing something is essential to being fulfilled, being at peace with yourself, and living in harmony with others. In other words, it is "Who before Do."

The Big Picture

I.   Who Am I in God's Eyes?

II. What Does This Mean to Me?

III. How Do I Live This Way?

IV. Power for Living

"I have a basic philosophy that I've tried to follow during my coaching career. Whether you're winning or losing, it's important to always be yourself. You can't change because of the circumstances around you."

Cotton Fitzsimmons,
college and NBA coach

What others say about us can begin to define us. We then attempt to live up to others' expectations of us. This is true whether the thoughts are from parents, others, or God Himself. Growing up, what were you told about who you are?

"If the words from parents, teachers, and friends are positive and in line with God's truth, they carry us through life to be blessed and productive. But if parents or teachers tell a child, "*You are worthless,*" "*You won't amount to anything,*" or, "*I hate you,*" rather than, "*I love you no matter what,*" then people struggle to overcome the impact of those negative words. Their emotional damage can curse a life, without the Truth of God." *John Beechner, CEO and owner of four businesses*

> ONLY CHRIST HIMSELF CAN LIVE THE CHRISTIAN LIFE, AND HE DOES THIS IN US AND THROUGH US.

I. Who Am I in God's Eyes?

When we come into this personal relationship with God through trusting who Christ is and what He has done for us, we move from the family of Adam to the family of God. We are adopted into God's family. What is significant about being an adopted child rather than one who is born into his family? Adoption is a relationship of choice. In our case, God's choice. We are not an "accident" or, worse, unwanted. When God says we are adopted into His family, that means we have gained a new identity, a new heritage and a new future. Examine the list on page 20. Reflect on who God says you are—your new identity.

REFLECT ON YOUR SENSE OF BEING *ACCEPTED* BY LOOKING AT JOHN 1:12 AND JOHN 15:15. WHAT DO THESE VERSES COMMUNICATE TO YOU ABOUT YOUR ACCEPTANCE?

_____

_____

_____

_____

REFLECT ON HOW *SECURE* YOU FEEL. HOW DO ROMANS 8:1-2 AND ROMANS 8:28 GIVE YOU A SENSE OF SECURITY? WHY IS SECURITY IMPORTANT?

_____

_____

_____

_____

EXAMINE JOHN 15:5 AND JOHN 15:16. HOW *SIGNIFICANT* ARE YOU IN GOD'S EYES? HOW SHOULD THIS CHANGE YOUR VIEW OF YOURSELF?

_____

_____

_____

_____

_____

Who I Am in Christ

> **I am accepted...**

John 1:12	I am God's child.
John 15:15	As a disciple, I am a friend of Jesus Christ.
Romans 5:1	I have been justified.
I Corinthians 6:17	I am united with the Lord, and I am one with Him in spirit.
I Corinthians 6:19-20	I have been bought with a price and I belong to God.
I Corinthians 12:27	I am a member of Christ's body.
Ephesians 1:3-8	I have been chosen by God and adopted as His child.
Colossians 1:13-14	I have been redeemed and forgiven of all my sins.
Colossians 2:9-10	I am complete in Christ.
Hebrews 4:14-16	I have direct access to the throne of grace through Jesus Christ.

> **I am secure...**

Romans 8:1-2	I am free from condemnation.
Romans 8:28	I am assured that God works for my good in all circumstances.
Romans 8:31-39	I am free from any condemnation brought against me and I cannot be separated from the love of God.
II Corinthians 1:21-22	I have been established, anointed and sealed by God.
Colossians 3:1-4	I am hidden with Christ in God.
Philippians 1:6	I am confident that God will complete the good work He started in me.
Philippians 3:20	I am a citizen of heaven.

> **I am significant...**

John 15:5	I am a branch of Jesus Christ, the true vine, and a channel of His life.
John 15:16	I have been chosen and appointed to bear fruit.
I Corinthians 3:16	I am God's temple.
II Corinthians 5:17-21	I am a minister of reconciliation for God.
Ephesians 2:6	I am seated with Jesus Christ in the heavenly realm.
Ephesians 2:10	I am God's workmanship.
Ephesians 3:12	I may approach God with freedom and confidence.
Philippians 4:13	I can do all things through Christ, who strengthens me.

Living Free in Christ, Neil Anderson

Our new identity is what we receive at the moment of salvation—new creation, new family, and new heritage. Our old nature has died and we now have a new nature (our position). As we grow, we begin to experience Christ living through us—this is known as Christ's indwelling life (our condition). Both are true and foundational to living the Christian life.

WHAT NEW INSIGHT DO YOU HAVE OF WHO YOU ARE IN GOD'S EYES AFTER READING II CORINTHIANS 5:17?

_____

_____

_____

_____

HOW DOES THIS DIFFER FROM WHAT YOU HAVE BEEN TOLD BY PARENTS OR OTHERS?

_____

_____

_____

_____

> "THE REALITY OF A NEW IDENTITY THROUGH THE IN-CHRIST RELATIONSHIP CAN DRAMATICALLY TRANSFORM US AS WE PROGRESSIVELY GRASP IT IN OUR EXPERIENCE. IT STRESSES THAT THE SPIRITUAL LIFE IS NOT A MATTER OF TRYING TO DO THINGS FOR JESUS, BUT CLAIMING AND RESTING IN WHAT HE HAS ALREADY DONE FOR US."
>
> Ken Boa, *Conformed to His Image*

II. WHAT DOES THIS MEAN TO ME?

Consider the Following:

"I cannot overly stress how critical it is to believe that God wishes all Christians would understand and appropriate their true identity in Christ. God wishes you, as a follower of Christ, would understand that your new identity is more than His having erased your name from the debit side of His ledger and moved it into the asset column. It is not a mere paper transaction. In order for God to write your name in the Lamb's book of life, a miraculous transformation must happen whereby you are instantly, radically changed:

The quality of your life is linked

to how well you understand your identity.

> From an enemy of God to a friend of God

> From a child of Satan to a child of God

> From not being accepted by God to being fully accepted by God

> From being guilty to being forgiven

> From being condemned to receiving a full pardon

> From being a glitch in God's vision to being the apple of His eye

> From being totally unlovely to being lovely and loveable

> From being a commoner to being royalty

> From focusing on being a sinner to focusing on being a saint

"All of this and much more become your permanent identity when you became spiritually reborn in Christ. He accomplished this all for you. Now He longs to reap the personal benefit from such a sacrifice by having a warm, intimate relationship with you."
Bill Gillham, speaker and author

IF WHAT THE ABOVE STATEMENTS SAY ABOUT THE "NEW YOU" IS ACCURATE, WHAT TRUE DIFFERENCE DOES THAT MAKE TO YOU?

_____

_____

_____

_____

THE STATEMENTS WERE ARRANGED BY THE CATEGORIES, HIGHLIGHTING THE FACT THAT WE ARE ACCEPTED, SECURE, AND SIGNIFICANT. IN YOUR EXPERIENCE, HOW ACCEPTED, SECURE, AND SIGNIFICANT DO MOST PEOPLE ACTUALLY FEEL?

_____

_____

_____

Do these adjectives describe you? Which ones?

_____

_____

_____

_____

Take it another step. These attributes of ours come from God. Because we are part of His family, we don't have to earn them or perform to keep them. What do you think about this fact?

_____

_____

_____

_____

A person's identity must be defined, not by success or even significance, but solely on the basis of Christ's sacrifice and His adoption of us into His family.

There is nothing I can do to make God love me any more, and there is nothing I can do to make God love me any less.

READ EPHESIANS 1:3-10. WHAT ARE THE QUALITIES OR BENEFITS OF BEING IN CHRIST?

_____

_____

_____

_____

Reflect on this quote:

"Our culture tells us that our worth is determined by our accomplishments and encourages us to pursue significance and meaning through the things we do. Scripture tells us that our worth is determined by what Christ was willing to do for us, and that in Him we have an unlimited and unchanging source of meaning and purpose. Who we are in Christ is not shaped by what we do, but by what He did on the cross and continues to do in our lives. It is not performance that determines our identity; instead, our new identity in Jesus becomes the basis for what we do. If we perceive ourselves to be worthless or inadequate, this will be manifested in our behavior.

"We honor God when we allow Him to define us and tell us who we are regardless of our feelings or experiences to the contrary. In Christ, we are overcomers who have been adopted into God's family; set free from the bondage to Satan, sin, and death; called and equipped to accomplish an eternal purpose that will have enduring results; raised up with Christ and partakers of His life."

> I AM FULLY RIGHTEOUS AT ALL TIMES, NOT ON THE BASIS OF MY WORK BUT BECAUSE OF CHRIST. MY IDENTITY AND SIGNIFICANCE ARE NEVER TIED TO PERFORMANCE, RESULTS, OR OUTWARD BEHAVIOR. I AM SIGNIFICANT BECAUSE OF WHO I AM IN CHRIST.

Ken Boa, *That I May Know God*

HOW DO THESE THOUGHTS IMPACT YOU PERSONALLY?

_____

_____

_____

_____

Summary

Christ's love and acceptance gives me security, significance and satisfaction.

> My worth and significance are found solely in Christ (which is forever and unchanging) and not in performance or in a position.

> Because of my worth in Christ, I am free from the opinions of others, though I can listen and learn from them.

> In this freedom from opinions, I can truly serve and love others. I can honor people.

> Because of my security in Christ, I can be process-focused vs. results-oriented or bottom-line-driven.

> Because of this freedom I possess, I can give away power or empower others, boldly and confidently.

> "In Christ" I am free from the bondage to sin. That means I am free from one of the chief sins: pride. I need not "think more highly of myself than I ought." (Romans 12:3)

> His love and acceptance give me a security which helps me examine and purify my motives.

III. How Do I Live This Way?

To know the truth about my identity is one thing, but how do I move the truth from my head to my heart and to my feet?

Jesus gives us a picture of this process in John 15. He describes the way we relate to Him in botanical terms. Just as a branch can be grafted into a vine, so we can be grafted into Him. Read John 15:4-5. What does the vine do for the branch? What does the branch do for the vine?

DESCRIBE THE RELATIONSHIP BETWEEN THE VINE AND THE BRANCH.

_____

_____

_____

_____

HOW MUCH CAN WE DO IN OUR OWN STRENGTH?

_____

_____

_____

_____

OUR OWN STRENGTH IS NEVER STRONG ENOUGH. HOW DOES THE IMPLICATION OF THAT STATEMENT
AFFECT YOU?

_____

_____

_____

_____

WHAT INSIGHTS CAN YOU APPLY TO YOUR RELATIONSHIP WITH CHRIST FROM JESUS' WORDS
IN MATTHEW 6:33-34?

_____

_____

_____

_____

IV. POWER FOR LIVING

The Indwelling Life of Christ – Christ in Me

We don't have the power to live the Christian life. Does that mean it's a hopeless pursuit? No. Christ Jesus defines who I am and provides hope, security, and acceptance. His life in me is the power I need to live the Christian life.

> GOD HAS GIVEN ME EVERYTHING TO SUCCESSFULLY AND SKILLFULLY LIVE THE CHRISTIAN LIFE.

LOOK AT GALATIANS 2:20. WHAT DID IT MEAN TO PAUL PERSONALLY THAT CHRIST LIVED IN HIM? WHAT DOES IT MEAN TO YOU?

_____

_____

_____

_____

_____

_____

STUDY PHILIPPIANS 1:21 AND COLOSSIANS 1:27-29. WHAT INSIGHTS DO YOU GAIN FROM THESE PASSAGES?

_____

_____

_____

_____

PAUL TALKED ABOUT HELPING OTHERS GROW IN THIS RELATIONSHIP WITH CHRIST IN THE FOLLOWING VERSES. WHAT DO HIS WORDS REVEAL ABOUT THE PROCESS OF GROWTH?

> II CORINTHIANS 12:9-11

_____

_____

_____

_____

_____

_____

"Your real, new self (which is Christ's and also yours, and yours just because it is His) will not come as long as you are looking for it. It will come when you are looking for Him....Give up yourself. And you will find your real self. Lose your life and you will save it.... Keep back nothing. Nothing that you have not given away will ever be really yours. Nothing in you that has not died will ever be raised from the dead. Look for yourself and you will find in the long run only hatred, loneliness, despair, rage, ruin, and decay. But look for Christ and you will find Him, and with Him everything else will be thrown in."
C. S. Lewis, *Mere Christianity*

Observations about Christ living in me:

> Christ in me provides unlimited, spiritual resources (wisdom, power) vs. relying on my limited, sometimes fleshly, resources. *II Corinthians 12:9-11*

> Through this indwelling, I can experience moment by moment victory (rest, peace) which comes from Him. *Ephesians 2:14-16*

> It provides and clarifies my true hope, especially in trial and difficulty. *Colossians 1:27-29*

> It is only Christ's resources that can defeat the true enemy—Satan. *I John 4:4*

> It is an ongoing and growing process. *Ephesians 4:13*

HOW DO WE LET THE SPIRIT OF CHRIST LIVE IN US AND THROUGH US?

_____

_____

_____

_____

WHY IS HUMILITY NECESSARY IN ORDER TO EXPERIENCE THIS?

_____

_____

_____

_____

Christ in me is the power to walk in victory and not in defeat.

A person joins God at work by allowing Christ's indwelling Spirit to flow through him. Christ in me is my source of wisdom and power.

Listen

Audio message for *Life Foundations*, Chapter 2, at www.operationtimothy.com or scan the QR code.

SCAN ME

Memory Verse: Our New Identity

II Corinthians 5:17

"Therefore, if anyone is in Christ, he is a new creation; the old has gone, the new has come!"

Additional Resources

> *Living Free in Christ*, Neil Anderson

> *Victory Over Darkness*, Neil Anderson

> *Classic Christianity*, Bob George

[OPTIONAL APPLICATION]

THINK: WHY IS IT SO HARD TO REALIZE WHAT I HAVE AND SO EASY TO FOCUS ON WHAT I NEED TO DO?

_____

_____

_____

_____

LISTEN: LISTEN TO THE AUDIO FOR _LIFE FOUNDATIONS_, CHAPTER 2, OR VISIT WWW.OPERATIONTIMOTHY.COM AND LISTEN TO SELECTIONS FOR THIS CHAPTER.

OBSERVE: WATCH THE 1979 FILM, _JESUS_, AND FOCUS ON THE RESURRECTION SCENE. CONSIDER HOW INADEQUATELY THE MIRACLE OF JESUS' LIFE-AFTER-DEATH IS PORTRAYED ON THE SCREEN. IMAGINE WHAT KIND OF POWER PERFORMED THE MIRACLE OF HIS RESURRECTION. THIS IS THE POWER THAT INDWELLS YOU!

_____

_____

_____

_____

CONSIDER: SUMMARIZE YOUR THOUGHTS ABOUT BEING IN CHRIST AND CHRIST IN YOU.

_____

_____

_____

_____

_____

_____

_____

NOTES

chapter 3

BATTLING THE WORLD, THE FLESH, AND THE DEVIL

That's What They Say

"The Church in the West today presents too easy a target for Satan. We do not believe we are at war. We do not know where the battleground is located, and, in spite of our weapons, they are neither loaded nor aimed at the right target. We are unaware of how vulnerable we are. We are better fitted for a parade than for an amphibious landing." *Ed Silvoso, speaker and businessman*

"Pride makes us artificial, humility makes us real." *Thomas Merton, priest*

"And Satan trembles when he sees the weakest saint upon his knees." *William Cowper (1731-1800), author*

"In general, pride is at the bottom of all great mistakes." *John Ruskin, author*

"There are two equal and opposite errors into which our race can fall about the devils. One is to disbelieve in their existence. The other is to believe, and to feel an excessive and unhealthy interest in them. They themselves are equally pleased by both errors." *C.S. Lewis, professor and author*

Wired for Battle

War is hell. That sentiment perhaps most accurately reflects the mood of our nation ever since the Vietnam War. Many agree this was a conflict without clear objectives or motives. General Maxwell Taylor, one of the principal architects of the war, called the Vietnam War "dirty business." No arguments there.

Dirty Business

Is this what spiritual warfare is? Do we embrace the amazing grace of God, enter into His eternal kingdom, become a member of a heavenly family, only to enlist the very next moment in the *dirty business* of war? Are we required to put our heads down and press on into the mud and muck of battle like a conscripted foot soldier who longs for home? Do we hear: "Accept God's bountiful love for you right where you are, but as soon as you do you'd better strap on your armor if you want to be good!"?

Or could it be that, like everything else in our lives, God's plan is to *redeem* the very idea of war? Just as He redeems broken things like relationships and work, might He be "buying back" the world's idea of conflict? If this is so, then the Christian's war might be an adventure rather than an obligation. If war is inevitable but redeemable, what does it look like from God's perspective?

"The generation that cannot be changed by the world is the generation that will change the world." *Ron Luce, businessman*

An Epic Battle

Little boys often dream of war. Even in homes where toy guns are forbidden, young boys will fashion just about any household item into a weapon. Clearly, little boys retain some of this mentality well into adulthood. Why else do war movies remain a wildly popular genre? Every culture in every time has an epic tale of combat in its history, whether legend or fact.

There is a noble place in our hearts that longs for battle. Could it be that God has put it there? That the battle is, indeed, a noble one because we are meant to fight it and we were made to win?

The Big Picture

In looking back on the Vietnam War, General Taylor observed "first, we didn't know ourselves... And we knew less about

AS FOLLOWERS OF CHRIST, WE ARE ENGAGED IN A COSMIC CONFLICT, WHETHER WE KNOW IT OR NOT. SCRIPTURE CLEARLY TEACHES AND ILLUSTRATES THE DYNAMICS OF THIS WARFARE ON THE THREE BATTLE FRONTS OF THE WORLD, THE FLESH, AND THE DEVIL. THE WORLDLY AND DEMONIC SYSTEMS ARE EXTERNAL TO BELIEVERS, BUT THEY ENTICE AND PROVIDE OPPORTUNITIES FOR THE FLESH, WHICH IS THE CAPACITY FOR SIN WITHIN US.

North Vietnam. Who was Ho Chi Minh? Nobody really knew. So, until we know the enemy and know our allies and know ourselves, we'd better keep out of this kind of dirty business."

In Chapter Two, we got to know ourselves, the first step in preparation for battle. In this chapter, we'll discover who our enemies are and how to vanquish them.

In this chapter we'll discuss the following topics:

   I. **What Is the Spiritual Battle?**

  II. **What Is Battle with the World?**

 III. **What Is Battle with the Flesh?**

 IV. **What Is the Battle with Satan?**

  V. **How Do We Have Victory?**

I. WHAT IS THE SPIRITUAL BATTLE?

READ CAREFULLY EPHESIANS 6: 10 – 19. WHAT DO YOU OBSERVE ABOUT THE WAR, THE PLAYERS, AND THE WEAPONS?

_____

_____

_____

_____

_____

Spiritual Warfare: What Is It?

Spiritual warfare exists in the unseen, supernatural dimension, where God is all-powerful and Satan is in revolt. As any Christian soon discovers, although spiritual warfare is unseen, it's absolutely real. The Bible speaks of spiritual warfare in many places, but most directly in Ephesians 6:12. *"For we wrestle not against flesh and blood, but against principalities, against powers, against the rulers of the darkness of this world, against spiritual wickedness in high places."*

battling the world, the flesh, and the devil

Although spiritual warfare is unseen, it's absolutely real.

Spiritual Warfare: Dress Code for a Soldier

In the 1850s, the rifle replaced the musket. And then several years later, smokeless powder was invented. Suddenly, visibility on the battlefield drastically improved. The color of uniforms became an issue of life or death. For obvious reasons, British infantrymen no longer wore their famous scarlet coats into combat by the 1890s. As Christians, what we wear into battle is just as important. Spiritual struggle requires specific arms and armor. Ephesians 6:13-18 offers a detailed description for the Christian's uniform and weaponry for combat:

> "Therefore put on the full armor of God, so that when the day of evil comes, you may be able to stand your ground, and after you have done everything, to stand. Stand firm then, with the belt of truth buckled around your waist, with the breastplate of righteousness in place, and with your feet fitted with the readiness that comes from the gospel of peace. In addition to all this, take up the shield of faith, with which you can extinguish all the flaming arrows of the evil one. Take the helmet of salvation and the sword of the Spirit, which is the word of God. And pray in the Spirit on all occasions with all kinds of prayers and requests. With this in mind, be alert and always keep on praying for all the saints."
> *Ephesians 6:13-18*

What is this Spiritual Armor? How does it apply to us?

Spiritual Warfare: Be Strong in the Lord

Spiritual warfare is a reality of the Christian life. But remember, we know the outcome already—our side wins the overall war. Since the devil has already lost, we can expect him to act with dangerous desperation, seeking to inflict as much damage as possible as he goes down.

> "Finally, be strong in the Lord and in his mighty power. Put on the full armor of God so that you can take your stand against the devil's schemes." *Ephesians 6:10-11*

RE-WRITE THIS VERSE AS A BATTLE SPEECH, AS IF YOU ARE A GENERAL PREPARING YOUR TROOPS FOR THE BATTLE. WHAT WOULD YOU SAY TO A UNIT OF SPIRITUAL SOLDIERS?

_____

_____

_____

_____

II. WHAT IS BATTLE WITH THE WORLD?

In this battle, there are several enemies. Each one tries to entice you to place value on something other than what is truly important. The first of these enemies is the world. Of course, the planet itself is not your enemy; but there are many things in the world that can lure your heart away from Christ. For this reason, we refer to them as "the world."

The state motto of North Carolina is *esse quam videri*, "to be rather than to seem." That phrase could be woven into a flag as the motto of every individual Christian as well. We aren't called to seem like anything. We're called to be who we truly are. The problem is, we live and work and eat and play in a world that is all about seeming. The world has it turned completely inside out; the unimportant is what matters in the world's value system.

In Psalm 90:1, Moses prayed, "Lord, through all the generations You have been our home!" (New Living Translation) This is from a man who wandered in the desert for forty years. But his words speak for every believer today: our true home is not the address listed on our mortgage. Like Moses, we're nomads. So when we speak of the gravitational pull of the world's temporal values and goals, we would do well to remember that the real world is another place altogether. And God's Word is a travel brochure to that real, substantial destination.

You Can't Get There from Here

When we are in bondage to "the elementary principles of the world" (Colossians 2:8), we cannot experience the freedom and joy that is waiting for us in our real "home" in Christ. When we buy into the world's standards of wealth, prestige, and position, we are subtly drawn away from the eternal value system revealed in Scripture. Worldliness isn't just what we drink, eat, and watch; it is an inner magnetism that lures us to conform to standards other than God's. It is a powerful force which has programmed much of our thinking from the moment of birth.

But just as our battle against the devil is already won, this battle—the battle to live above what is seen— is a done deal. We already live there. We just need to open our eyes and look around.

REVIEW EPHESIANS 6:12. WHO IS BEHIND THE FORCES OF THIS WORLD?

_____

_____

_____

_____

LOOK AT I JOHN 2:15-17. WHAT ARE THE THREE ELEMENTS OF THE WORLD THAT WE STRUGGLE WITH?

_____

_____

_____

HOW HAVE YOU EXPERIENCED THE GRAVITATIONAL PULL OF THE WORLD'S SYSTEM?

_____

_____

_____

_____

_____

READ ROMANS 12:1-2. HOW DO THESE VERSES APPLY TO OUR WAR WITH THE WORLD?

_____

_____

_____

_____

Otherworldly peace isn't a prize reserved for mystics and monks. Yes, the ancients meditated on the vanity of the world, the brevity of life, and the eternality of the life to come, and the practice led many to hide from the world in caves and convents. But when we transfer our hope and identity to the enduring promises of God alone, we transcend our earthly environment. It's a choice. "Choose for yourselves today whom you will serve" (Joshua 24:15).

EXERCISE: REFLECT ON THE FOLLOWING PASSAGES TO NOTE HOW THEY RELATE TO OUR CONFLICT WITH THE WORLD SYSTEM: LUKE 9:23-25; JOHN 17:14-17; PHILIPPIANS 4:8

_____

_____

_____

_____

III. What Is the Battle with the Flesh?

Perhaps you read about who you are in Christ in the previous chapter and thought, "But that's not my experience. I don't look like that!" If you feel that disconnect between truth and experience, you're not alone. As you read the next passages, you'll discover that there's more to come! We are still waiting for the fullness of our redemption (Romans 8:23). Until that time, the old appetites, attitudes, memories, and habits can surface at any time and wage war against the life of Christ in us.

If our battle against our flesh were merely outward in nature, the world's monasteries would be full. We'd still be wearing hair shirts and practicing self-flagellation, but the reason these extremes aren't necessary isn't the fact the battle is inner rather than outer. The reason is who we are and whose we are. Philippians 2:13 promises: "For God is working in you, giving you the desire to obey him and the power to do what pleases him." The desire you need to defeat the flesh is already inside you. This is one of the ways God has redeemed the concept of war for Christians. He has caused us to yearn for the fight.

Study Romans 7:22-23. What do these verses say about the nature of the inward conflict?

_____

_____

_____

_____

Paul speaks about the flesh in Galatians 5:19-21. What are some of the manifestations of the flesh?

_____

_____

_____

_____

Which, if any, do you struggle with?

_____

_____

_____

_____

_____

WHERE DO WE BEGIN TO FIGHT THE ENEMY ON THIS FRONT? LOOK AT THE FOLLOWING PASSAGES AND NOTE A HELPFUL APPLICATION FROM EACH.

> ROMANS 6:6-7

_____

> ROMANS 6:12-13

_____

> ROMANS 8:12-13

_____

> GALATIANS 5:16,25

_____

IV. WHAT IS THE BATTLE WITH SATAN?

A Little Name-Calling

Satan means "the adversary." But he has many other names and descriptions in Scripture. Let's see what we can learn about him through some of them.

REFERENCE:	How Satan is described:
Matthew 13:19	_____
John 8:44	_____
John 16:11	_____
II Corinthians 4:4	_____
I Thessalonians 3:5	_____
I Peter 5:8	_____
Revelation 12:3-9	_____

Satan's Strategy

Smooth Operator. We've learned much about Satan from his biblical names and descriptions. We can learn even more from observing him in action. Let's observe two particular case studies:

Case Study A: Adam and Eve

Read Genesis 3:1-5. You might recall that the first man and woman were given one command: not to eat of one particular tree.

IN VERSE 1, WHAT QUESTION DOES SATAN POSE TO EVE?

_____

_____

EVE REPEATED GOD'S WORDS, ADDING HER OWN TWIST. ACCORDING TO EVE, GOD SAID NOT TO EVEN TOUCH THE FRUIT. IN VERSES 4 – 5, HOW DOES THE SERPENT RESPOND?

_____

_____

_____

Case Study B: Jesus

Jesus is sometimes called "the Second Adam" (see Romans 5). He, too, faced Satan's deception. Read Matthew 4:1-11.

HOW DOES SATAN FIRST TEMPT JESUS? (V.3)

_____

_____

_____

IN VERSES 5 – 6, WHAT DOES THE DEVIL USE TO ENTICE JESUS?

_____

_____

_____

IN VERSES 8 – 9, WHAT ARE THE STAKES?

_____
_____
_____

WHAT PERSONAL GOAL DOES SATAN REVEAL?

_____
_____
_____

IN ALL CASES, HOW DOES JESUS COUNTER TEMPTATION?

_____
_____
_____

IN THESE TWO STUDIES, WHAT PARALLELS CAN YOU FIND IN THE DEVIL'S STRATEGY?

_____
_____
_____
_____

IN LUKE 22:31, HOW IS SATAN'S WORK DESCRIBED?

_____
_____
_____
_____

Now we know something about how Satan works. Forewarned is fore-armed! But we need a cohesive battle plan. In the next section, we'll put one together.

V. How Do We Have Victory?

Playing Defense

EPHESIANS 4:27 MENTIONS ANOTHER DEFENSIVE FORMATION. WHAT DO YOU THINK PAUL IS REFERRING TO?

_____

_____

_____

HOW IS SATAN DESCRIBED IN 1 PETER 5:8-9?

_____

_____

_____

_____

WHAT IS HELPFUL ABOUT THE KNOWLEDGE DESCRIBED IN VERSE 9?

_____

_____

_____

_____

The Last One Standing

In the legend of Robin Hood, a hulking man named Little John plays a supporting role as the strongest of the Merry Men. He isn't the ultimate hero, Robin is. The story might have turned out differently based on one little chapter at the beginning of the tale. When the two men duel with their quarterstaffs on a bridge in Sherwood Forest, Robin is unceremoniously dumped in the creek. But we know how the story ends. Robin Hood gets all the glory as the leader of his Merry Men and defeater of the wicked Sheriff of Nottingham.

We may lose our foothold and fall, but we know that God is ultimately in control. He will be victorious over the Enemy, and He will get the glory.

Taking the Offense

FINALLY, THERE ARE SOME THINGS CHRISTIANS CAN DO TO TAKE THE BATTLE TO THE EVIL ONE. READ REVELATION 12:11. WHAT ARE THE WEAPONS WHICH OVERCOME SATAN?

_____

_____

_____

JAMES 4:7 TELLS US TO SUBMIT OURSELVES TO GOD. ACCORDING TO I JOHN 2:3-4, WHAT IS THE INDICATOR OF OUR SUBMISSION?

_____

_____

_____

HOW CAN OBEDIENCE TO GOD'S COMMANDMENTS THWART THE DEVIL'S WORK?

_____

_____

_____

_____

The Scouting Report

REFLECT ON THE WEEK (OR "WEAK"?) AHEAD. WHERE ARE YOUR PRESSURE POINTS? DECIDE ON SOME TIMES AND PLACES YOU WOULD EXPECT SATAN TO LOOK FOR A FOOTHOLD. WHAT OFFENSIVE AND DEFENSIVE STRATEGIES WILL FORM AN EFFECTIVE GAME PLAN FOR YOU?

_____

_____

_____

_____

The Final Score

An enthusiastic football fan records the games of his favorite team. He sweats through the actual contests, but he enjoys the recording. "It's amazing how much stress is removed when you know how it all comes out," he smiles.

The Bible records all the game highlights of our history—past, present, and future. The winner has been decided. For those of us who are believers, the game must still be played every day, but we can play it with excitement and confidence when we know the final score. God wins—and so do we.

"We know that the whole creation has been groaning as in the pains of childbirth right up to the present time. Not only so, but we ourselves, who have the firstfruits of the Spirit, groan inwardly as we wait eagerly for our adoption as sons, the redemption of our bodies." *Romans 8:22-23*

> "'When the Son of Man comes in his glory, and all the angels with him, he will sit on his throne in heavenly glory. All the nations will be gathered before him, and he will separate the people one from another as a shepherd separates the sheep from the goats.'" *Matthew 25:31-34*

"And I heard a loud voice from the throne saying, 'Now the dwelling of God is with men, and he will live with them. They will be his people, and God himself will be with them and be their God. He will wipe every tear from their eyes. There will be no more death or mourning or crying or pain, for the old order of things has passed away.'" *Revelation 21:3-4*

"Therefore, my dear brothers, stand firm. Let nothing move you. Always give yourselves fully to the work of the Lord, because you know that your labor in the Lord is not in vain."
I Corinthians 15:58

Memory Verse: Battling the World, the Flesh, and the Devil

I Peter 5:8-9

> "Be self-controlled and alert. Your enemy the devil prowls around like a roaring lion looking for someone to devour. Resist him, standing firm in the faith, because you know that your brothers throughout the world are undergoing the same kind of sufferings."

Listen

Audio message for *Life Foundations*, Chapter 3, at www.operationtimothy.com or scan the QR code.

Audio 1　　　Audio 2

Additional Resources

> *The Screwtape Letters*, C.S. Lewis

> *The Strategy of Satan*, Warren Wiersbe

[OPTIONAL APPLICATION]

THINK: Do you live aware of this battle or oblivious to it?

_____

_____

_____

_____

_____

OBSERVE: Watch *The Lion, The Witch, and The Wardrobe* based on C.S. Lewis' classic children's book. How does the white witch personify our spiritual enemy?

_____

_____

_____

_____

_____

CONSIDER: As a child, what was your perception of the devil?

_____

_____

_____

_____

_____

NOTES

DEALING *chapter 4*
WITH TEMPTATION

That's What They Say

"Tis one thing to be tempted, another thing to fall." *William Shakespeare, English playwright*

"Obedience is the key to all doors; feelings come (or don't come) and go as God pleases. We can't produce them at will and mustn't try." *C. S. Lewis, professor and author*

"I can resist everything except temptation." *Oscar Wilde, author*

"There are several good protections against temptation, but the surest is cowardice." *Mark Twain, humorist and author*

"Better to shun the battle than struggle in the snare." *John Dryden, playwright*

"Man will do in the presence of God, what he will never do in the presence of men." *Walt Henrichsen, author and lecturer*

Crossroads

"S.O.S. I need your help. I am injured, near death, and too weak to hike out of here. I am all alone, this is <u>no joke</u>. In the name of God, please remain to save me. I am out collecting berries close by and shall return this evening. Thank you, Chris McCandless. August"

Christopher McCandless graduated from Emory University in 1990, gave his entire savings to charity, and began a two-year trek across the country as "Alex Supertramp." When his desperate note was discovered by two hikers on the door of an abandoned bus near Denali National Park in Alaska, he wasn't out foraging for berries, he was inside in his sleeping bag.

He had been dead of starvation for at least two weeks.

McCandless believed he could rely on his meager supplies and his severely limited education and experience to survive in the wild. By the time he made a choice to cry out for help, it was too late.

That's what temptation can do. We can be right at the edge of a breathtakingly beautiful wilderness and totally miss it! The Christian life isn't a walk down a garden path—but it isn't a trudge in the mud either. It's often a hike on a difficult trail, and the view from the trail is stupendous! You wouldn't want to miss it for the world. Could it be temptation is more than just a lure toward bad habits and moral failings? Could it be the choice temptation presents to us isn't even an enticement to actually leave the trail?

Christopher McCandless' journey into the wilds of Alaska missed the mark of his original dream, not because he caved in and gave up. He missed fulfillment of his purpose simply because he waited too long to acknowledge his own helplessness.

"I know of no other way to triumph over sin long-term than to gain a distaste for it because of a superior satisfaction in God."

John Piper, Desiring God

The Big Picture

At several points during his long journey, Christopher McCandless was offered assistance... and rejected it. Help was available. But his stubborn refusal to accept help turned what could have been an adventure into a nightmare. Consider this chapter a travel guide through the rough terrain of temptation. We'll examine four areas pertaining to obedience, temptation, and confession:

I. **Understanding Temptation**

II. **How Can I Find the Path Again?**

III. **How Do I Stay on the Path?**

IV. **The Fruits of Obedience**

> TEMPTATION IS UNUSUAL—
> IT IS ALWAYS PRESENT, WE
> ARE THE LAST TO SEE IT, AND
> IT IS STRONGEST WHEN WE
> ARE ALONE.

I. UNDERSTANDING TEMPTATION

The Deceit of Desire

READ JAMES 1:13-15. WHAT IS THE SOURCE OF TEMPTATION?

_____

_____

_____

_____

IS THERE A DIFFERENCE BETWEEN SIN AND TEMPTATION? IF SO, HOW WOULD YOU DELINEATE BETWEEN THE TWO?

_____

_____

_____

_____

ACCORDING TO THESE VERSES, HOW CAN TEMPTATION CAUSE US TO BE "DRAGGED AWAY" FROM THE RIGHT PATH?

_____

_____

_____

_____

WHAT DO YOU FIND MOST DIFFICULT WHEN YOU ARE FACED WITH A TEMPTATION?

_____

_____

_____

_____

Behind every temptation is a spiritual prison cell

awaiting its taker.

HOW DO YOU FEEL WHEN YOU FAIL?

_____

_____

_____

_____

A Path Out

WHAT THREE ASSURANCES ABOUT TEMPTATION ARE GIVEN IN I CORINTHIANS 10:13?

_____

_____

_____

_____

The Voice of Experience

READ HEBREWS 4:14-16. WHAT HELP DOES JESUS PROVIDE IN OUR TEMPTATIONS?

_____

_____

_____

_____

ACCORDING TO VERSE 16, WHAT SHOULD YOU DO WHEN YOU FACE TEMPTATION?

_____

_____

_____

_____

II. How Can I Find the Path again?

Call It Like It Is

There's a reason men are universally known for refusing to ask for directions. At some point we have to get back on the right road. One of life's toughest assignments is admitting when we're wrong—or that we're lost. When we sin we have a choice: confess and receive forgiveness, or disagree with God and face the consequences of guilt and broken relationships—things we were made to avoid.

"Confession" makes us think of the desperation of a death row inmate or the quiet seclusion of a shadowed confessional booth. We've all heard the phrase "confession is good for the soul." But what does that mean? Let's find out what Scripture says about it.

WHAT TWO PURPOSES ARE GIVEN FOR CONFESSION IN I JOHN 1:9?

_____

_____

_____

_____

IN I JOHN 2:12, WE SEE THAT ACTUALLY OUR SINS ARE ALREADY FORGIVEN. WHY, THEN, IS IT IMPORTANT THAT WE CONFESS OUR SINS?

_____

_____

_____

_____

HOW DO WE FIND THE RIGHT PATH?

_____

_____

_____

_____

Don't Go It Alone

SO, IS THAT ALL THERE IS TO CONFESSION? IS IT MERELY A PRIVATE MATTER? READ JAMES 5:16. WHAT TWO ACTIVITIES ARE DESCRIBED?

_____

_____

_____

_____

_____

DO YOU HAVE ACCESS TO THE KIND OF CHRISTIAN FRIEND DESCRIBED HERE?

_____

_____

WRITE THE NAME(S) OF A PERSON(S) WITH WHOM YOU CAN SHARE DEEP NEEDS AND PRAY.

_____

_____

_____

_____

WHAT HELP HAVE YOU FOUND IN CONFESSING YOUR FAULTS OR WEAKNESSES TO OTHERS?

_____

_____

_____

_____

Discuss with your partner in this discipleship process each other's struggles and how are you working through them.

III. How Do I Stay on the Path?

God will not leave us in the woods. He promises to help us find our way out. It's one thing to speak of obeying one's parents, a supervisor, or the authorities. We can see and hear them. But how exactly do we obey God? How can we know we're on the "straight and narrow" path? Look at II Timothy 3:16.

1. Teaching

(What to believe and do) Shows you the path to walk on.

2. Rebuking

(Recognizing sin) Shows you where you've gotten off the path.

3. Correcting

(How to change) Shows you how to get back on the path.

4. Training

(How to live) Shows you how to stay on the path.

How would you restate this in your own words?

_____

_____

_____

_____

Jesus says His sheep will hear His voice and follow. We hear Him speak in Scripture and through prayer. We follow the example of Jesus Himself. We seek the counsel of wise Christians. He will always be there to provide clear guidance. The question is generally not one of understanding, but of the will. In the next section we will explore what happens when we stray from the path.

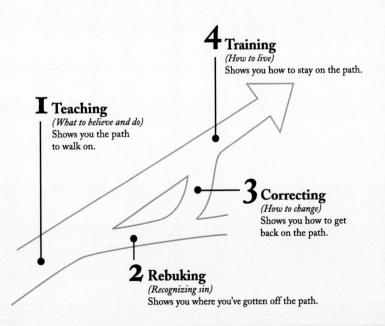

READ JOHN 10:27. WHAT DOES JESUS SAY HIS FOLLOWERS WILL DO?

_____

_____

_____

_____

WHAT DOES PSALM 119:11 POINT OUT THAT WE CAN DO?

_____

_____

_____

_____

HOW, IN YOUR OPINION, CAN MEMORIZING SCRIPTURE ENCOURAGE US TO BE OBEDIENT?

_____

_____

_____

_____

I JOHN 2:6 FOCUSES ON ANOTHER WAY WE CAN BE OBEDIENT. WHAT IS IT?

_____

_____

_____

_____

AFTER REVIEWING PHILIPPIANS 3:16, WHY IS OBEDIENCE CRITICAL?

_____

_____

_____

_____

OBEDIENCE IS A MATTER OF BODY, SOUL, MIND, AND SPIRIT. HOW DOES ROMANS 6:12-14 SAY WE CAN BE OBEDIENT WITH OUR BODIES?

_____

_____

_____

WHAT AREAS OF YOUR LIFE DO YOU FEEL THIS PASSAGE APPLIES TO?

_____

_____

_____

_____

_____

MATTHEW 7:7 GIVES A SIMPLE APPROACH FOR FINDING GOD'S WILL. IN YOUR OWN WORDS, EXPLAIN JESUS' TEACHING IN THIS VERSE.

_____

_____

_____

_____

ANOTHER IMPORTANT ELEMENT OF OBEDIENCE IS FOUND IN PROVERBS 13:20. WHY DO YOU THINK THIS INSTRUCTION IS IMPORTANT?

_____

_____

_____

_____

IV. The Fruits of Obedience

If only obedience came naturally! Anyone who has ever been a parent (or a child) knows that it doesn't. Children are born with an inclination to rebel. It has been this way since Adam and Eve failed their first test. At some point, in so many words, kids ask the question: "Why obey my parents?" Whether we're comfortable admitting it or not, Christians eventually need to ask a similar question. We need to understand the why, as well as the what, of obedience.

WHAT SIMPLE MOTIVATION FOR OBEDIENCE IS GIVEN IN JOHN 14:21?

_____

_____

_____

_____

HOW DOES LOVE RESULT IN OBEDIENCE?

_____

_____

_____

_____

_____

_____

_____

READ AGAIN JOHN 14:21. WHAT FURTHER DEVELOPMENTS SPRING FROM LOVING OBEDIENCE?

_____

_____

_____

_____

_____

PSALM 119:9 TELLS US THAT OBEYING GOD WILL HELP US KEEP OUR WAY PURE. HOW DOES THIS WORK?

_____

_____

_____

_____

MATTHEW 7:24-27 OFFERS A PARABLE OF JESUS. SUMMARIZE THE MESSAGE OF THIS STORY IN YOUR OWN WORDS.

_____

_____

_____

Hope for Us

In the Old Testament, King David was tempted and he fell into a wrong relationship with another man's wife, Bathsheba, with grievous consequences. When confronted with this, he acknowledged the wrong and repented.

LOOK AT ACTS 13:22 WHAT DOES GOD SAY ABOUT DAVID AND HOW WOULD THIS GIVE YOU HOPE?

_____

_____

_____

Displacement

Our brains are powerful instruments, that's why the medical definition of death is "no brain activity." The human brain contains more than 100 billion neurons, each linked to as many as 10,000 other neurons. Although we're capable of multi-tasking, or parallel thought processes, our powerful brains still function best when we focus. We take supplements and go to seminars to learn the art of focusing. That's because what we think about either limits or expands what we're able to do. From the first day of kindergarten, we experience the necessity of focus. By middle school, we've learned that the grades on our report cards are linked to our ability to focus. According to the commercials, any bad habit from overeating to smoking can be conquered with enough of this desirable brain function. So how do we focus?

Try this simple exercise: Think about the number four. Take a few seconds to focus on four. Got that cemented in your mind? Okay, now stop thinking about four. Get rid of that four! It's hard to do, isn't it? Finally, take a moment to think about the number six. Six. Focus on six. If your brain functions like most people's, you are now thinking of six instead of four. You've demonstrated the handy skill of displacement.

Philippians 4:8 says, "Finally, brothers, whatever is true, whatever is noble, whatever is right, whatever is pure, whatever is lovely, whatever is admirable—if anything is excellent or praiseworthy—think about such things."

Paul's admonition is to fill your mind so full of what is true and good, sinful thoughts are displaced. Temptation will come, but it's hard for the devil to deceive you when your mind is focused on excellent things. Satan can only work with what you give him, so don't give him any opportunity to work on your mind.

This isn't just passive mental manipulation. It's capitalizing on the way God made your mind. Here are a couple of basic exercises (so basic, it's almost embarrassing) that demonstrate our ability to "renew" our thinking. For two weeks, make a list every morning of ten things you're thankful for. At the end of the two weeks, look back and observe any overall changes in your attitudes in general.

Here's another: When you are tempted in a certain area, use the moment to pray for a friend who you know struggles with similar temptations. It is amazing how the temptations ease up when you shift your focus to someone else's need.

Follow the Leader

Obedience isn't the result of sheer willpower. For someone who has experienced the grace of God, it is an ongoing, profound "thank you" note to the Giver of that grace. It is grateful communication that ultimately leads to intimacy with the one we're thankful to. Not only that, obedience to God is the only sane way to live in the world He created. Every other path leads to self-destruction. As you travel, always keep in mind Paul's words:

> "Never be lacking in zeal, but keep your spiritual fervor, serving the Lord. Be joyful in hope, patient in affliction, faithful in prayer." *Romans 12:11-12*

"I NEED HELP! The words screamed at my mind as I hurried out of a Reno, Nevada casino. Since arriving I had denied that I had a gambling problem. I was a Christian, an active member of my church, but I had a problem I wasn't aware of. Everyone else knew. They knew why I quit my job-training program to commit myself to the outpatient program at the state hospital. They knew why I was over my head in debt. They knew I wrote bad checks to casinos. Everyone knew, but me." — *Member of Gamblers Anonymous*

Perhaps the most poignant and powerful prayer of all is the "I need help" prayer. When we say these words to God we acknowledge our desperate need for Him to come rescue us. Colossians 2:6 says, "As you have received Christ Jesus, so walk in Him." What did your first prayer to Him sound like? How is that first experience of crying out to God similar to your daily walk with Him now?

Memory Verse:
Dealing with Tempation

I Corinthians 10:13

> "No temptation has seized you except what is common to man. And God is faithful; He will not let you be tempted beyond what you can bear. But when you are tempted, He will also provide a way out so that you can stand up under it."

"Victory in the Christian life is not me overcoming sin. Victory is Christ overcoming me."

Wayne Barber, pastor and author

REFLECT BACK ON THIS STUDY. WHAT NEW INSIGHTS DID GOD REVEAL TO YOU?

_____

_____

_____

_____

Listen

Audio message for *Life Foundations*, Chapter 4, at www.operationtimothy.com or scan the QR code.

 SCAN ME   SCAN ME

Audio 1   Audio 2

Additional Resources

> *Everyman's Battle*, Stephen Arterburn and Fred Stoeker

> *A Journey to Victorious Praying*, Bill Thrasher

[OPTIONAL APPLICATION]

THINK: READ II CORINTHIANS 3:18. SHOULD WE FOCUS ON NOT SINNING OR KNOWING GOD?

_____

_____

_____

_____

OBSERVE: WATCH *THE MISSION*. HOW IS CONFESSION AND REPENTANCE DEPICTED IN THE FILM? WHAT ABOUT THE MESSAGE IS TRUE AND BIBLICAL? WHAT IS NOT?

_____

_____

_____

_____

CONSIDER: READ HEBREWS 12:1-13. WHAT IS ENCOURAGING TO YOU IN THIS PASSAGE?

_____

_____

_____

_____

WHAT IS DIFFICULT FOR YOU IN THIS PASSAGE?

_____

_____

_____

_____

NOTES

chapter 5

That's What They Say

"Very few seem to be interested in the Holy Spirit… Why, were it not for the work of the Holy Spirit there would be no gospel, no faith, no Church, no Christianity in the world at all." *J.I. Packer, theologian and author*

"The Holy Spirit has long been the Cinderella of the Trinity. The other two sisters have gone to the theological ball; the Holy Spirit got left out every time." *Alister McGrath, author*

What's in a Name?

God's name is so familiar in our culture that many make use of it in daily conversation. The problem is they summon God by name most vehemently when they swear. When your neighbor bangs his thumb with a hammer in his garage, he might just invoke God's name loudly enough for you to hear it in your living room. The same goes for Jesus. If your buddy laments a fumble during Monday Night Football, Jesus may be mentioned. But even those who use salty language probably don't call upon the Holy Spirit with the same ease.

Whether they know Him or not, most people are comfortable using God's name in conversation. But not the Holy Spirit. He's the neglected Person of the Trinity. Even His name is mysterious. The King James version of the Bible refers to Him as The Holy Ghost. Talk about spooky! For many believers, His work is equally obscure. Who is He? What does He mean to your life? The Bible has plenty to tell us about the Holy Spirit.

The Big Picture

In this section we'll examine four questions:

I. Who Is the Holy Spirit?

II. Who Has the Holy Spirit?

III. What Does the Holy Spirit do?

IV. How Does One Live and Walk with the Holy Spirit?

I. WHO IS THE HOLY SPIRIT?

The Holy Spirit Is a Person

Sometimes a young husband will refer to his unborn child as "it." That's because, unlike his wife, he doesn't yet have a felt connection with his son or daughter. The connection just isn't quite there. But when he first holds their

"The Christian Life is the life of Christ in us; without a moment-by-moment reliance on the Holy Spirit, this level of living is impossible."

Ken Boa, author

newborn in his arms, he or she will never again be an "it." Now, he sees his son or daughter as a real person.

Isn't this how we often talk about the Holy Spirit? We're not comfortable or familiar enough with Him to refer to Him any other way than "it." The Scripture never makes this mistake. The Holy Spirit is always described in the Bible as a "He." He is one of the three Members of the Triune God. While we worship one Lord, He is expressed as Father, Son, and Holy Spirit. We are intimately connected to Him. And once we know Him, things will never be the same again.

READ GENESIS 1:2 AND COMMENT ON THE DESCRIPTION OF GOD'S SPIRIT.

_____

_____

_____

_____

BECAUSE HE IS GOD, THE SPIRIT HAS ALWAYS BEEN IN EXISTENCE. READ ANOTHER PASSAGE FROM OLD TESTAMENT TIMES (BEFORE JESUS), PSALM 139:7-8. WHERE IS THE SPIRIT, ACCORDING TO THESE VERSES?

_____

_____

_____

Low Key, High Power

The Tarbela Dam is the largest earth-filled dam in the world. It is so massive that lettering engraved upon it can be seen from space. The dam, which sits on the Indus river in Pakistan, is the primary source for all of the country's hydroelectric capacity. Yes, it's large. But the majority of the people who benefit from the Tarbela have never seen it. Nor can they see the electricity it provides. Talk with the residents of Lahore, almost 1000 km away, about the electricity they use every day and most likely the conversation will be about their bill or problems with service. Chances are, no one will mention the Tarbela Dam. But that doesn't matter. The source of all that power keeps working, whether it is acknowledged by its benefactors or not.

THERE'S NO DOUBT THE HOLY SPIRIT SEEMS TO KEEP A LOWER PROFILE THAN THE FATHER OR THE SON. BUT HIS POWER IS UNDENIABLE. HOW DOES JESUS DESCRIBE THE CHARACTER OF THE HOLY SPIRIT IN JOHN 16:13-14?

_____

_____

_____

To fully comprehend the Trinity is beyond the capacity of our finite minds. But God has designed His creation to give us some pictures that help our understanding. Look at the following lists and allow the images of a man, an egg, and water to round out your understanding of the Trinity.

ONE MAN	ONE EGG	WATER	MAN
Three functions	*Three parts with three distinct purposes*	*Three states*	*Three parts*
> Father to his children	> Shell – For protection	> Liquid	> Body
> Son to his parents	> White – For nourishment	> Vapor (steam)	> Soul
> Husband to his wife	> Yolk – For fertilization	> Solid (ice)	> Spirit

Get the Picture

The Holy Spirit never speaks of Himself. But what is He like? Let's look at some of the symbols used for Him in Scripture.

WHAT IMAGE IS ASSOCIATED WITH THE SPIRIT IN I THESSALONIANS 5:19?

_____

WHAT IMAGE IS ASSOCIATED WITH THE SPIRIT IN JOHN 7:38-39?

_____

WHAT IMAGE IS ASSOCIATED WITH THE SPIRIT IN JOHN 1:32?

_____

II. WHO HAS THE HOLY SPIRIT?

Here to Help

READ JOHN 16:7. WHAT DOES THIS VERSE TELL US ABOUT JESUS' REGARD FOR THE HOLY SPIRIT ('COUNSELOR')?

_____

_____

_____

_____

IN YOUR OPINION, WHAT IS THE ADVANTAGE OF HAVING THE HOLY SPIRIT INSTEAD OF THE PHYSICAL PRESENCE OF JESUS?

_____

_____

_____

_____

READ JOHN 7:38-39. FOR WHOM IS THE SPIRIT AVAILABLE?

_____

_____

_____

_____

ACCORDING TO VERSE 39, WHY HAD THE SPIRIT NOT BEEN PREVIOUSLY AVAILABLE?

_____

_____

_____

_____

HOW WOULD ONE KNOW IF THE HOLY SPIRIT WAS WORKING IN SOMEONE'S LIFE?

_____

_____

_____

_____

Spiritual hunger, spiritual questions and discernment are just a few signs of God working.

Your Heart, a Home for God

READ I CORINTHIANS 3:16. WHY IS IT IMPORTANT THAT GOD DWELLS IN US AND WE ARE DESCRIBED AS HIS TEMPLE?

_____

_____

_____

_____

God has chosen to dwell, in Spirit,

inside the hearts of His followers.

What if you discovered that the President of the United States was coming to visit your home? "Curb appeal" would take on a new meaning, wouldn't it? Would you do a thorough cleaning? Buy new furniture? Paint that room you've been meaning to paint? Would you worry about having everything at its best? The Bible tells us that God Himself, in the Holy Spirit, is your permanent guest!

Not for Everyone

We must also ask who does not have the Holy Spirit.

IN JOHN 14:17, WHY DO PEOPLE REJECT THE SPIRIT?

_____

_____

_____

_____

_____

IN JOHN 5:40, WHY DO SOME PEOPLE NOT RECEIVE THE LIFE THE HOLY SPIRIT OFFERS?

_____

_____

_____

_____

READ I CORINTHIANS 2:14-16. DESCRIBE THE DIFFERENCE BETWEEN ONE WHO HAS THE SPIRIT AND ONE WHO DOESN'T.

_____

_____

_____

_____

He is as powerful as fire, as life-giving as water, as gentle as a dove, and brings the very anointing of God. We need to know more about this Spirit.

III. WHAT DOES THE HOLY SPIRIT DO?

Role

The ministry of the Holy Spirit has three primary aspects: bearing witness to Jesus Christ, applying Christ's redemptive work in human hearts, and working personally and progressively to form Christ-likeness in the lives of believers. Now we know who the Holy Spirit is and that He is available to all believers. Exactly what does He set out to accomplish?

READ JOHN 14:26. WHAT PURPOSE IS STATED FOR THE SPIRIT?

_____

_____

_____

_____

HOW WOULD YOU SUMMARIZE THE RELATIONSHIP BETWEEN JESUS AND THE SPIRIT?

_____

_____

_____

_____

READ JOHN 16:7-15. WHAT DOES THIS HAVE TO DO WITH US?

_____

_____

_____

_____

WHAT DOES VERSE 13 SAY THE HOLY SPIRIT WILL DO FOR US?

_____

_____

_____

_____

WHAT STARTLING CLAIM IS MADE ABOUT THE SPIRIT IN VERSES 14 – 15?

_____

_____

_____

_____

I CORINTHIANS 2:10-16 DEVELOPS THIS IDEA FURTHER. WHAT UNIQUE POWER IS DESCRIBED IN VERSES 10 – 11?

_____

_____

_____

_____

_____

_____

ACCORDING TO VERSE 13, WHAT DOES THE HOLY SPIRIT GIVE US?

_____

_____

_____

WHAT ATTRIBUTE DOES THE SPIRIT BRING TO US, ACCORDING TO ACTS 1:8?

_____

_____

_____

"A full-orbed spirituality involves grounding in biblical truth and sound doctrine (*knowing*), growing character and personal experience with God (*being*), and developing gifts and skills in the service of others (*doing*). When a person or a group neglects any one of these three areas, distortions are inevitable." Ken Boa, *Conformed to His Image*

KNOWING

KNOWING – Spirit – Motivation

BEING – Gifts – Ministry

DOING – Fruit - Manifestation

BEING   DOING

HOW DOES ONE KEEP THIS IN BALANCE?

_____

_____

_____

_____

WHAT HAPPENS WHEN THESE GET OUT OF BALANCE?

_____

_____

_____

_____

_____

Gifts for Everyone

The Spirit is also the distributor of wonderful gifts. The chart below lists some of them. The gifts are often defined and grouped in various ways. Here is one way of looking at some of the gifts that the Holy Spirit gives to believers.

SPEAKING GIFTS

Prophecy	Speaks biblical truth	Romans 12:6
		I Corinthians 12:28
		Ephesians 4:11
Teaching	Presents truth practically	Romans 12:7
		I Corinthians 12:28
		Ephesians 4:11

SERVICE GIFTS

Serving	Desires to help others	Romans 12:7
Giving	Gives generously	Romans 12:8
Administration	Organizes well; productive	I Corinthians 12:28
Helps	Desires to help meet needs	I Corinthians 12:28

RELATIONAL GIFTS

Encouragement	Builds up; edifies others	Romans 12:8
Leadership	Motivates others	Romans 12:8
Mercy	Sympathetic, tolerant	Romans 12:8
Shepherding	Caring and nurturing	Ephesians 4:11
Evangelism	Passion to share the gospel	Ephesians 4:11

If you have not identified your own spiritual gift(s), there are several excellent resources that provide a personal questionnaire to help you discern what they might be and how God might want to use your gifts to benefit the body of Christ and the world.

LOOK AT 1 PETER 4:10-11. WHAT DO WE LEARN IN THESE VERSES ABOUT SPIRITUAL GIFTS?

_____

_____

_____

_____

_____

_____

Ask your Paul what spiritual gifts he sees in you. Discuss how God may use your gifts in His Kingdom.

IV. HOW DOES ONE LIVE AND WORK WITH THE HOLY SPIRIT?

Getting Your House in Order

A guest has come to stay in your home—indefinitely. This makes him a permanent part of your household, a part of the family! In order to accommodate your guest, you begin a total reorganization of your home. It's the same way with the Holy Spirit. As we have seen, God now considers your body His temple. We might certainly behave differently in a place of worship than, say, a gymnasium.

READ ROMANS 6:11-14. WHAT IS THE BASIC CHANGE WE SHOULD CONSIDER?

_____

_____

_____

_____

HOW ARE WE TO LIVE WITH THIS NEW RESIDENT?

_____

_____

_____

WHAT KIND OF OFFERING SHOULD WE MAKE TO GOD IN THE "TEMPLE"?

_____

_____

_____

_____

DESCRIBE SOME OF THE GOOD ACTIVITIES FROM THIS PASSAGE WHICH MAY APPLY TO YOUR LIFE.

_____

_____

_____

_____

Fresh Fruit in Season

If you are planning a trip that includes a long stay in a friend's home, you will most likely take them a gift. That's what thoughtful guests do. You may even consider your host's unique needs and tastes. Need ideas? Simply Google "hostess gift." You'll find over two-million links to gift-selling sites. One major evidence of the Holy Spirit's presence are the gifts He brings when He comes to stay. He is a guest who truly beautifies His surroundings.

READ GALATIANS 5:19-25. LIST THE FRUIT. DOES THE LIST IN VERSES 19 – 21 REMIND YOU OF TODAY'S WORLD? EXPLAIN.

_____

_____

_____

_____

WHY DO YOU THINK PAUL REFERS TO THE LIST IN VERSES 22 – 23 AS "FRUIT"?

_____

_____

WHAT DOES HE MEAN BY THE PHRASE "KEEP IN STEP WITH THE SPIRIT?" (V.25)

_____

_____

WHAT TRUTH ABOUT THE HOLY SPIRIT FROM THIS STUDY HAS MOST ENCOURAGED YOU? EXPLAIN YOUR ANSWER.

_____

_____

Jesus' followers must have been shocked when He said they would be better off if He left, yet we understand what He meant. The presence of the Holy Spirit means Christ lives within us. We have His mind, His guidance and power, wherever we go and for always. Yet despite this, we need each other all the more—the Spirit brings us together to be the Body of Christ and gives us gifts with which we build each other up. Indeed we continue learning to keep in step with the Spirit.

Memory Verse: Discovering the Holy Spirit

Galatians 5:22-23

"But the fruit of the Spirit is love, joy, peace, patience, kindness, goodness, faithfulness, gentleness and self-control. Against such things there is no law."

Listen

Audio message for *Life Foundations*, Chapter 5, at www.operationtimothy.com or scan the QR code.

Audio 1   Audio 2

Additional Resources

> *Absolute Surrender*, Andrew Murray

> *The Fruit of the Spirit*, John Sanderson

[OPTIONAL APPLICATION]

THINK: WHAT DOES GALATIANS 5:24 SAY A CHRIST-FOLLOWER HAS DONE? HOW IS THE HOLY SPIRIT HELPING YOU WITH THIS?

_____

_____

_____

OBSERVE: ASK FIVE PEOPLE TO DESCRIBE THE HOLY SPIRIT IN ONE SENTENCE. HOW MANY OF THEIR DESCRIPTIONS ARE SIMILAR? HOW MANY GAVE CONFUSING ANSWERS?

_____

_____

_____

CONSIDER: A CHECKUP FROM THE NECK UP. READ EPHESIANS 4:23-32. LIST SOME OF THE NEW ATTITUDES AND APPROACHES GOD INTENDS FOR YOUR LIFE, ACCORDING TO THIS PASSAGE.

_____

_____

_____

WHAT DO YOU THINK IT MEANS TO "GRIEVE THE HOLY SPIRIT," BASED ON VERSE 30?

_____

_____

THE "SEAL" IN VERSE 30 MEANS A PLEDGE—IN MODERN BUSINESS TERMS, A LETTER OF INTENT. THE HOLY SPIRIT IS GOD'S MARK ON A PERSON'S LIFE. WHAT IS YOUR REACTION TO THIS IDEA?

_____

_____

NOTES

COMMUNICATING WITH GOD

chapter 6

That's What They Say

"Pray as though everything depended upon God. Work as though everything depended on you." *St. Augustine, theologian*

"I watched the deckhands on the great liner, United States, as they docked that ship in New York Harbor. First, they threw out a rope to the men on the dock. Then inside the boat, the great motors went to work and pulled on the great cable. But oddly enough, the pier wasn't pulled out to the ship; but the ship was pulled snugly up to the pier. Prayer is the rope that pulls God and man together. But it doesn't pull God down to us; it pulls us to Him." *Billy Graham, evangelist*

"Prayer is not designed as a means for us to change God. It is a time for God to change us." *Richard Blackaby, author*

"A Christian without prayer is just as impossible as a living person without a pulse." *Martin Luther, theologian*

"Is prayer your steering wheel or your spare tire?" *Corrie ten Boom, Holocaust survivor*

A Tragic Disconnect

Most parents' anticipation of their child's first word is rewarded sometime around the son or daughter's first birthday. Before long, there are more words and then fragments and then whole sentences. By the time bubbling paragraphs full of run-on sentences become commonplace, mom or dad might wish for a few moments of silence. Even so, parents love to hear their children's voices.

That's why autism is so heartbreaking. For the parents of an autistic child, the longing for communication can feel like a cheap trick. God made us with ears to listen to our children, yet these parents are cheated out of the prize. The usual interchange between a mother and son or a father and daughter, complete with silly words and laughter, is typically absent where autism is present in the home. Silence is often a tragic hallmark of the disease—silence that can't be broken by ordinary means.

These days, parents and educators and medical professionals are working hard to raise our awareness about autism. Doctors are lobbying for earlier testing. Educators are launching schools and programs just for autistic kids. And parents—hurting, caring, creative parents—are doing everything in their power to make autism an easier verdict for families. Petting zoos, animal assistance programs, books and websites, all represent volunteerism at its best. It's the parents who are making the biggest difference. And why not? They are the ones who care the most.

"I have been driven many times to my knees by the overwhelming conviction that I had absolutely no other place to go."

Abraham Lincoln, President of USA

Made to Connect

We all know prayer is communication with God. We study it, talk about it, read about it. But, if we're really honest, we would all admit how difficult prayer actually is. We make lists and set our clocks and study it some more, but still prayer doesn't come easily. We even get on our knees... and fall asleep. We say, "I'll pray for you," then forget to do it. What's wrong with us?

One of the tragic effects of sin is our inability to communicate with God. As Christians, we sense that our silence hurts our Father. This knowledge may even make prayer seem more daunting. The good news is, He's more compassionate than any father here on earth. Yes, He longs to hear us speak, but He also understands how hard it can be for us to utter the simplest of phrases to Him. Yes, He made us with a capacity for conversation, and His plan is to redeem and repair that basic instinct. Could it be we're treating prayer like a discipline rather than a God-given impulse? Prayer is much more than a discipline. It is the miracle God intended to break the silence between His heart and ours.

Where Do You Rate?

Mark the selection below that best describes your prayer relationship with God:

O He walks with me and He talks with me.　　O I'm lousy at keeping in touch.

O We check in daily.　　O I've lost the address!

O We touch base from time to time.　　O Other

The Big Picture

   I. **What Are the Essentials of Prayer?**

  II. **What are the Benefits of Prayer?**

 III. **For Whom Do We Pray?**

 IV. **How Do We Spend Time with God?**

I. WHAT ARE THE ESSENTIALS OF PRAYER?

God has broken the silence between us by speaking through His Word, by sending His Son. The Father has initiated the communication, and prayer is our response. It's a miraculous connection. And, often, when we first begin the conversation, it seems to come naturally. So why all the emphasis on discipline? Why the plethora of helps for those who are serious about prayer?

Romance, in the beginning, has no requirements. Communication happens easily between those who are newly in love. In fact, for the couple who are smitten with each other, it's hard to imagine ever having to work at their relationship. But at some point, if the romance flourishes and leads to marriage, discipline becomes necessary. Not always, but sometimes. There are just too many distractions in everyday life. Too many ways to lose sight of the main thing.

Sure, prayer is intimate, but it still involves discipline. And discipline is the tether that keeps the conversation going when all else fails.

Why, When, and How

WHY SHOULD WE PRAY, ACCORDING TO HEBREWS 4:16? AND WITH WHAT ATTITUDE?

_____

_____

WHAT DIFFERENCE DOES IT MAKE TO YOU WHETHER YOU PRAY OR NOT?

_____

_____

_____

If we're really honest,

we would all admit how difficult prayer actually is.

WHEN SHOULD WE PRAY, ACCORDING TO I THESSALONIANS 5:17?

_____

_____

_____

_____

PRACTICALLY, WHAT DOES THIS MEAN?

_____

_____

_____

_____

PSALM 62:8 AGREES WITH THAT LAST VERSE, AND ADDS A DESCRIPTION OF HOW WE SHOULD PRAY. RESTATE THAT COMMAND IN YOUR OWN WORDS.

_____

_____

_____

_____

Friendly chat. Serious discussion. Conflict management. Playful flirting. When you know someone intimately, you eventually run the gamut of these types of conversation.

LOOK UP THE FOLLOWING VERSES AND MAKE NOTE OF THE PRIMARY FOCUS OF EACH VERSE AS IT RELATES TO PRAYER.

> I Samuel 12:23

_____

> Psalm 38:18

_____

> Ephesians 5:20

> James 1:5

The following verses give insight into the depth and breadth of prayer.

> John 16:24 Ask in Jesus' name, and you will receive, that your joy may be complete.

> I John 5:14-15 If we ask anything according to His will, He hears us, and we know that we have what we asked of Him.

> Matthew 21:22 If you believe, you will receive whatever you ask for in prayer.

> John 15:7 If I remain (abide) in Jesus and Jesus abides in me, I will receive whatever I ask.

> Psalm 66:18 If I cherish sin in my heart, God will not listen.

> James 4:3 We ask and do not receive, because we ask with wrong motives, to spend on our own selfish desires.

> Psalm 46:10 Be still, and know that I am God.

Praying without ceasing seems impossible, but it is similar to breathing and thinking at the same time.

What about unanswered prayer? Little children ask for many things which their parents believe would be unwise to give them. Our heavenly Parent, God, knows much better then we do what our needs are, and when they should be met. Everyone has prayed in some urgent or desperate circumstance, and failed to receive what they asked for. We tend to call this "unanswered prayer," but it's more accurate to say that the answer isn't the one we preferred. God answers every prayer—the mature Christian seeks to draw closer to Him to better understand those answers.

The Perfect Script

Jesus' friends once asked Him to teach them to pray. In Matthew 6:9-13, He gave us a model prayer. Study that prayer carefully.

WHAT ARE THE GOD-CENTERED REQUESTS?

_____

_____

_____

_____

_____

WHAT ARE THE PERSONAL REQUESTS?

_____

_____

_____

_____

WHY DO YOU THINK JESUS USED THIS PARTICULAR ORDER?

_____

_____

_____

_____

IN THE SPACE BELOW, TRY REWRITING JESUS' PRAYER USING YOUR OWN WORDS, THOUGHTS AND REQUESTS.

_____

_____

_____

_____

_____

Filling in the Blanks

We need discipline in order to pray. We don't need it every day, but we often do. The danger in discipline is that it can lead to an auto-pilot approach. It can turn something dynamic into a static structure. Instead of pouring out our hearts to God, we can begin speaking as if our Bibles are teleprompters. How can we avoid dryness in our prayer lives?

WHO HELPS US PRAY, ACCORDING TO ROMANS 8:26, AND HOW?

_____

_____

_____

_____

WHAT DOES ROMANS 8:5 HAVE TO DO WITH PRAYER?

_____

_____

_____

_____

II. WHAT ARE THE BENEFITS OF PRAYER?

Great Benefits

The benefits of good communication may best be understood by observing what happens in a relationship without it. When two people don't talk, they never get to know each other, they have no basis for resolving conflict, and they can't deepen the relationship. But when they do talk, the opposite is true, the union flourishes and grows. It's even possible to experience personal growth because of our interaction with others. We say things like, "I am a better person because of you," and it's true. But there's a limit to what communication can do, unless the conversation is with God.

When we talk with God, we get to know Him better. Our relationship with Him thrives. But the benefits of prayer extend far beyond that. Unlike a human relationship, this is a union with the God of the Universe. It stands to reason that conversation with *Him* would impact our lives in incredible ways. Read on to discover just a taste of what His power can do when activated by our prayer.

WHAT MOTIVATION TO PRAY CAN WE FIND IN JEREMIAH 33:3?

_____

_____

_____

_____

ACCORDING TO PSALM 34:4, WHAT DOES GOD DO FOR US THROUGH PRAYER?

_____

_____

_____

_____

PAUL, THE WRITER OF PHILIPPIANS, WAS A PRISONER WHO COULD HAVE EASILY COINED THE PHRASE "STRESSED OUT." IN PHILIPPIANS 4:6-7, WHAT IS HIS PRESCRIPTION FOR ANXIETY?

_____

_____

_____

_____

WHAT CAN WE EXPECT WHEN WE PRAY THIS WAY?

_____

_____

_____

_____

_____

_____

_____

GOD KNOWS EVERYTHING ALREADY, OF COURSE. WHY WOULD HE WANT US TO PRAY ABOUT "EVERYTHING?"

_____

_____

_____

_____

REFLECT ON ONE AREA IN YOUR OWN LIFE ABOUT WHICH YOU'D LIKE TO EXPERIENCE THIS PEACE. DESCRIBE IT BELOW.

_____

_____

_____

_____

III. FOR WHOM DO I PRAY?

Praying for Others

When the Spirit gets involved, we understand His priorities and we find ourselves praying for others.

WHAT SPECIAL GROUP DOES PAUL PRAY FOR IN ROMANS 10:1?

_____

_____

_____

READ MATTHEW 9:37-38. WHY WOULD JESUS ASK THE DISCIPLES TO PRAY FOR LABORERS?

_____

_____

_____

_____

ACCORDING TO I TIMOTHY 2:1-4, WHO ELSE CAN YOU PRAY FOR?

_____

_____

_____

_____

WHAT KIND OF PERSON DOES LUKE 6:28 INDICATE WE SHOULD PRAY FOR?

_____

_____

_____

_____

THIS IS TOUGH! WHY SHOULD WE DO IT?

_____

_____

_____

PAUL'S ELOQUENT PRAYER IN EPHESIANS 3:14-21 CAN BE APPLIED TO PEOPLE ON YOUR PRAYER LIST. IN FACT, PRAYING SCRIPTURE BACK TO GOD IS A WONDERFUL WAY TO COMMUNICATE WITH HIM.

_____

_____

_____

HAVE YOU EVER FELT LIKE GOD DOESN'T HEAR YOUR PRAYERS? WHAT DOES I PETER 3:7 HAVE TO SAY ABOUT THAT?

_____

_____

_____

_____

Making a List and Checking It Twice

When your calendar is full of errands and appointments, you make a list. You can't afford to forget even one responsibility. After all, most of your obligations ultimately impact people. If you slack off in your business,

your family eventually suffers. The same with your bills. If you're late to a meeting, others are inconvenienced. So you write it down and follow through.

In the same way, your prayer life is a responsibility that impacts people. As you schedule a daily prayer time, have a prayer notebook with you in which you can jot down requests. It can serve as a handheld device that reminds you to pray. And you can also keep track of the answers to your prayers—that's the exciting part. Your prayer list might include some or all of the following:

> Family members

> Non-Christian acquaintances

> Pastor and Church

> People at work

> Problem relationships

> Governmental authorities

> Missionaries and Christian workers

> Personal needs

Here is a sample of the "10 Most Wanted" card (available from CBMC at www.cbmc.com). This card is a tool to help you pray for the people you know who need to know Christ. Write down the names of those individuals you intend to pray for regularly. Consider additional ways God might use you to help them cultivate a growing relationship with Christ. Keep the card handy and refer to it whenever you spend devotional time with God.

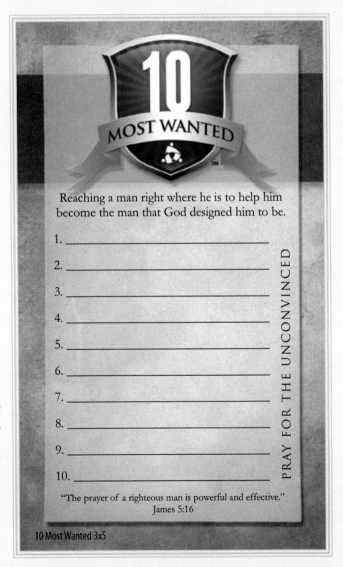

10
MOST WANTED

Reaching a man right where he is to help him become the man that God designed him to be.

1. _____
2. _____
3. _____
4. _____
5. _____
6. _____
7. _____
8. _____
9. _____
10. _____

PRAY FOR THE UNCONVINCED

"The prayer of a righteous man is powerful and effective."
James 5:16

10 Most Wanted 3x5

Too Busy Not to Pray

We've all said this: "Prayer is great. I just have trouble finding the time." The truth is, we always find time for the things that are important to us. Our hearts prioritize our agendas.

IN LUKE 10:38-42, STUDY THE CONTRASTING AGENDAS OF TWO WOMEN, MARY AND MARTHA. WRITE YOUR OBSERVATIONS ABOUT THEIR ACTIVITIES BELOW.

_____

_____

_____

_____

HOW DID JESUS RESPOND TO THEIR APPROACHES?

_____

_____

_____

_____

_____

LIST THE ACTIVITIES MOST LIKELY TO DISTRACT YOU FROM SPENDING TIME WITH GOD.

_____

_____

_____

_____

WHAT CAN YOU DO SPECIFICALLY TO OVERCOME SOME OF THESE DISTRACTIONS?

_____

_____

_____

_____

WHAT IS THE MOST EXCITING NEW TRUTH YOU'VE LEARNED IN THIS SESSION? WHAT IS THE GREATEST CHANGE YOU EXPECT TO MAKE IN YOUR PRAYER LIFE?

_____

_____

_____

_____

IV. HOW DO WE SPEND TIME WITH GOD?

Quiet Time

Much has been written for believers to help them have a fruitful and effective quiet time. These quiet times have truly been daily spiritual food for many, yet many others have felt guilty or somehow inferior for their inconsistency or lack of focus. Our goal is not to burden you with a task, but to deepen your intimacy with God.

Why Have a Quiet Time?

David, in Psalm 27:8, says, "My heart says of you, 'Seek His face!' Your face, LORD, I will seek." God called David to seek His face. God desires our presence—much like a father desires to be with his children. This is our motivation: to be with God. He wants us!

A quiet time is a meeting with our Lord—to hear from Him, to call out to Him, to be with Him. David expresses his heart to be with God in Psalm 27:4: "One thing I ask of the Lord, this is what I seek: that I may dwell in the house of the Lord all the days of my life, to gaze upon the beauty (delightfulness) of the Lord and to seek Him in His temple." David wanted one thing of God—to be with God, to know and love God, to consider His ways. This was his heart's desire. It was a yearning, a thirst. It was his highest priority. The psalmist in Psalm 42:1 illustrates this: "As the deer pants for streams of water, so my soul pants for You, O God."

What Is a Quiet Time?

> A special time to meditate and reflect on God's Word for inspiration, guidance, hope.

> A time to hear from God. "Call to Me and I will answer you and tell you great and unsearchable things you do not know" (Jeremiah 33:3).

> A time to pray for the lost (10 Most Wanted).

> A time to call upon God in prayer.

> Pray Scripture back to God.

ACTS: *Adoration, Confession, Thanksgiving, Supplication*

Many Christians have found the letters ACTS helpful in praying. The letters stand for Adoration, Confession, Thanksgiving, and Supplication (requests). This is a sensible sequence; we get everything in perspective by adoring and praising God for who He is. Focusing on God reveals our own inadequacies and failures, and we confess them. As we do this, we know God forgives us, and as we feel a refreshing sense of thanksgiving, we begin to express our gratitude for His many blessings. Finally, with the Spirit's assistance, we can properly ask Him to supply our needs and the needs of others.

ACTS is not a list of "to dos." It is a guideline to help focus our prayers.

When?

Whenever you so desire! Many have found it beneficial to greet the Lord early in the morning, before they engage in daily activities. Many of the Psalms encourage this. Others have found that night time may be more suitable for them. Any time is good—the point is to do it. Yet, don't feel guilty if you miss this time. Consistency comes with growth, practice, and maturity.

How?

Ten to fifteen minutes may be a realistic goal to begin with. You may want to eventually lengthen this time. You might spend it in the following way:

> Five minutes of prayer

> Five minutes of Bible reading

> Five minutes of reflection/meditation

Find a quiet place, free from distractions. You may want to be at a table, desk, or favorite reading chair in order to be able to write and reflect.

Some Practical Suggestions to Get Started

You can read through the Psalms in a month by reading five psalms a day. You can also read through Proverbs in a month, one chapter a day. Several Bibles are available that are designed to help you read through the Bible in a year. This usually takes only 15 – 20 minutes a day of reading. *The Daily Walk Bible* published by Walk Thru the Bible Ministries is available in several translations and gives an overview of the day's reading, insight into some of the history and other background, and helps in applying Scripture to daily life. There are also many reading plans freely available online. Your Paul may have a couple he can recommend.

Do you currently have a plan for spending time with God? If not, what will you do to begin?

_____

_____

_____

_____

Consider finding an accountability partner: someone with whom you are open and honest about your time with the Lord, your needs, hurts and prayers.

Memory Verse:
Communicating with God

Philippians 4:6-7

"Do not be anxious about anything, but in everything, by prayer and petition, with thanksgiving, present your requests to God. And the peace of God, which transcends all understanding, will guard your hearts and your minds in Christ Jesus."

Listen

Audio message for *Life Foundations*, Chapter 6, at www.operationtimothy.com or scan the QR code.

Audio 1   Audio 2

Additional Resources

> *Prayer: A Holy Occupation*, Oswald Chambers

> *Letters to Malcolm: Chiefly on Prayer*, C.S. Lewis

[OPTIONAL APPLICATION]

THINK: WHY DOES GOD ANSWER MY PRAYERS?

_____

_____

_____

_____

_____

OBSERVE: WATCH FRANK CAPRA'S CLASSIC FILM, *IT'S A WONDERFUL LIFE*. HOW DOES GEORGE BAILEY'S PRAYER NEAR THE BEGINNING OF THE FILM ILLUSTRATE A HEALTHY WAY TO PRAY? HOW DOES IT ILLUSTRATE AN UNHEALTHY MANNER OF PRAYING?

_____

_____

_____

_____

_____

CONSIDER: READ MATTHEW 6:9-13 ("THE LORD'S PRAYER") IN AS MANY TRANSLATIONS AS YOU CAN FIND. (WWW.BIBLEGATEWAY.COM HAS QUITE A FEW.) WHAT ELSE CAN YOU LEARN FROM JESUS' TEMPLATE FOR US?

_____

_____

_____

_____

_____

NOTES

chapter 7

TELLING OTHERS OUR STORY

That's What They Say

"Every believer should be a witness. In fact, every believer is a witness whether he wants to be or not. An impression goes out from every one of us concerning what we believe." *Donald Grey Barnhouse, pastor*

"How can we [Christians] be the salt of the earth if we never get out of the salt shaker?" *Rebecca Manley Pippert, author*

"Preach the gospel at all times, and when necessary use words." *commonly attributed to Francis of Assisi, monk*

"Evangelism is just one beggar telling another beggar where to find bread." *D. T. Niles, missionary*

"The salvation of a single soul is more important than the production or preservation of all the epics and tragedies in the world." *C.S. Lewis, professor and author*

The Allure of a Good Story

Just when we thought the television sitcom was a dying genre, along came a show about... nothing. Instead of telling the contrived tales of co-workers or family members, Jerry Seinfeld and Larry David concocted a program based on the shaky premise that millions of viewers just might find real life minutiae of four friends in the upper west side of Manhattan interesting. The sitcom focused its drama on riveting subjects like waiting in line at restaurants, going to the dentist, or finding a parking space. And it ran for nine successful seasons and won an

unprecedented ten Emmy awards. All proof of the attraction of a story.

The setting and the characters may vary, but the *story* is what fascinates us. That's why we have an undeniable urge to tell our stories. Whether our alma mater just won the NCAA basketball championship or our puppy did a new trick. Whether we won an all-expense-paid cruise in a lottery or something funny happened at the grocery store. We want to tell about our day and our life, and the people who know us usually want to hear.

Spread the Word!

We all have a story. Some are glamorous, some very difficult, and some are plain vanilla. If we know Jesus Christ, we have a story of epic and eternal proportions. It doesn't matter whether we quietly turned to Christ as a young child or dramatically returned from a life of rebellion as an adult. The story is essentially the same—we were dead and now we are alive! How much more powerful could a story be?

"Our business is to present the Christian faith clothed in modern terms, not to propagate modern thought clothed in Christian terms. Confusion here is fatal."

J.I. Packer, theologian and author

The Big Picture

In this lesson, we'll discuss the art of sharing wonderful news. We'll discuss four categories:

I. **What Is My Testimony?**

II. **Why Should I Tell Others?**

III. **What Should I Say?**

IV. **Who Should I Tell?**

I. What Is My Testimony (*A REAL LIFE STORY*)?

Putting Your Story to Work

"I wish I could turn this conversation around and tell him about Christ."

"If there were only more time, I could tell him what Christ means to me."

"I wish I could remember those verses about how someone can receive Christ."

"If Paul were here, he could really explain how to become a Christian."

Have these thoughts ever crossed your mind as you have had opportunities to share Christ? You can turn day-to-day situations into exciting opportunities to share your faith by preparing ahead of time. In I Peter 3:15, Peter admonished us to be ready:

> *"But in your hearts set apart Christ as Lord. Always be prepared to give an answer to everyone who asks you to give the reason for the hope that you have."*

Any subject can be presented more effectively by careful organization. A carefully prepared testimony, given in the power of the Holy Spirit, can be of immediate and effective use in nearly every witnessing situation. It should be our desire to present Christ in such a clear and attractive, yet simple, way that those who hear will not only want to know Him, but they will want to know Him in a personal way.

A carefully worded, concise testimony will communicate far more effectively than a prolonged presentation that includes a lot of extraneous material. The key is to minimize details that detract from, rather than emphasize, the point of personal commitment to Christ and what this can mean in a person's life. What are the essentials for effectively presenting the gospel? Fortunately, God has left us a model to follow. In Acts 26, we find Paul before King Agrippa, in the act of giving his testimony. Read Acts 26 before going on. Here are a few ways that you might personalize these same principles in your own testimony.

> "The skeptic may deny your doctrine or attack your church but he cannot honestly ignore the fact that your life has been changed. He may stop his ears to the presentations of a preacher and the pleadings of an evangelist, but he is somehow attracted to the human-interest story of how you—John Q. Public—found peace within.
>
> Charles Swindoll, *Come Before Winter*

1. Gracious Introduction

Acts 26:2, 3: "…I consider myself fortunate to stand before you today as I make my defense…"

DESCRIBE PAUL'S ETIQUETTE IN VERSES 2 AND 3.

_____

_____

_____

_____

Notice that Paul referred to Agrippa's knowledge of Jewish customs. In the same way, find a point of common interest or identification. You might say to a friend, "You and I have a lot in common, Pete. When I started my career, I had everything a fellow could want, but underneath there was a lot of dissatisfaction." If the person has children, something along the following lines might be appropriate: "Bringing up children in this modern world is nearly impossible. Apart from one fact I'd be utterly lost." You should have several possible introductions that you could use in a variety of situations.

2. Good Part of Past Life

Acts 26:4, 5: "…I lived as a Pharisee…"

WHAT IS PAUL'S STRATEGY IN THESE VERSES?

_____

_____

_____

_____

If you just say what a sinner you were, people won't identify themselves with you. Paul told how he was respected for his religious practices. If relevant, briefly mention your good points from a worldly sense, like morality, church attendance, ideas about God, generosity, as you lead to the third point.

3. Bad Part of Past Life

Acts 26:9-11: "…I, too, was convinced that I ought to do all that was possible to oppose the name of Jesus…"

How does Paul attempt to intrigue his listeners in verses 9 – 11?

_____

_____

_____

_____

Mention some specific things that plagued your life before you met Christ, such as hateful thoughts, covetousness, emptiness of heart, or pride. You could say, "Even though people thought I was good person, I knew what went on inside of me." Perhaps you feared that you would not go to heaven. Many will identify with you in this—they're not sure they're going to heaven either.

4. Circumstances of Conversion

Acts 26:12-15: "Who are you, Lord?"

What were some of the personal details that Paul included in his story?

_____

_____

_____

_____

Don't feel your own story is colorless compared to Paul's. Your conversion is as much a miracle as his. Your testimony doesn't have to be exciting, just interesting and real to your audience. Use details which show the personal transaction with God, and avoid confusing statements like "I went forward at church," lest your listener thinks going forward is the answer. Instead, use, "When the minister asked if I had received Christ personally, I knew that I had not and that this was the time I must trust Him." If you do not know the exact time you accepted Christ's forgiveness, you could say: "The time came when I realized what I was doing was not enough, but that Jesus' death on the cross provided my salvation." We know the sun rises at an exact moment, but we may not have seen it right then. Yet we know it is there because we see it in the sky.

5. Results of Conversion

Acts 26:19: "I was not disobedient to the vision from heaven."

WHAT WERE SOME OF THE RESULTS OF PAUL'S ENCOUNTER WITH JESUS?

_____

_____

_____

_____

Mention the most striking change in your life, as Paul did—whether in desires, actions, hunger for God's Word, peace, or satisfaction. Show the effects of your being born-again. Be realistic. Don't imply that Christ eliminates all the problems of life, but rather that He enables you to live them out with peace and confidence.

6. Gospel Message

Acts 26:23: "that the Christ would suffer and, as the first to rise from the dead..."

WHY IS IT IMPORTANT THAT PAUL INCLUDED THIS IN HIS STORY?

_____

_____

_____

_____

Christ's story, His death for our sins, and His resurrection must be woven into your story. Without His resurrection, you would not have a story worth telling, so emphasize that accepting Jesus Christ as Lord and Savior caused the difference in your life.

The order of Paul's story reflects the situation he was in and the people he was speaking to. Your message must have this type of flexibility. For example, you may find it beneficial to include the gospel explanation in point four, making it part of the explanation of how you came to Christ. This portion of your testimony should include Scripture verses.

7. Personal Appeal

Acts 26:29: "That...you may become what I am..."

How does Paul make his case to Festus in verses 24-27?

_____

_____

_____

_____

Using the listener's name, ask a question relating to him. "Bob, have you ever thought of Christ in this personal way?" Or, "Does what I've said bring any questions to your mind?"

Now, you're ready to prepare your story.

Use the three-point outline below (before, how, after) to quickly list the major points as they come to mind. When you write it out in more detail, keep it between 700 and 1000 words (if typewritten, about four double-spaced pages). This will allow you to stay within three to five minutes when you give it verbally. Many have found it helpful to take a first-pass at their testimony verbally and have a friend identify and jot down the major points on the outline.

As you begin, ask God to give you the right words and approach. Trust Him to do it. This is as much His story as it is yours.

Personal Testimony Sheet

I. Before:

1. What were some of your personal goals in life before you became a Christian?

_____

_____

_____

_____

Without Christ's resurrection,

you would not have a story worth telling.

2. WHAT WERE SOME OF THE THINGS THAT CAUSED YOU TO BEGIN CONSIDERING A PERSONAL RELATIONSHIP WITH JESUS CHRIST FOR YOURSELF? (GOOD PART OF PAST LIFE; BAD PART OF PAST LIFE)

_____

_____

_____

_____

3. BEFORE YOU MADE THE DECISION TO BECOME A CHRISTIAN, WHAT DID YOU KNOW ABOUT A PERSONAL RELATIONSHIP WITH JESUS CHRIST?

_____

_____

_____

_____

4. HOW DID YOU LEARN OR HEAR ABOUT HOW TO BECOME A CHRISTIAN?

_____

_____

_____

_____

_____

_____

5. AFTER YOU KNEW HOW TO BECOME A CHRISTIAN, IF YOU PUT OFF MAKING THAT DECISION FOR A PERIOD OF TIME, WHAT WERE THE THINGS THAT CAUSED YOU TO PUT IT OFF?

_____

_____

_____

_____

6. WHAT SPECIFIC THING CAUSED YOU TO DECIDE TO GIVE YOUR LIFE TO CHRIST?

_____

_____

_____

_____

II. How:

1. WHO WERE YOU WITH WHEN YOU MADE THE DECISION TO INVITE CHRIST INTO YOUR LIFE?

_____

_____

_____

_____

2. WHERE WERE YOU WHEN YOU MADE THAT DECISION?

_____

_____

_____

_____

3. WHEN OR ABOUT WHEN IN YOUR LIFE DID YOU MAKE THAT DECISION?

_____

_____

_____

_____

4. WHAT WERE THE WORDS YOU SAID WHEN YOU PRAYED TO BECOME A CHRISTIAN?

_____

_____

_____

_____

III. After:

1. ONCE YOU INVITED CHRIST INTO YOUR LIFE, WHAT WERE YOU AWARE OF AT THAT MOMENT?

_____

_____

_____

_____

2. WHAT SPECIFIC NEEDS DID JESUS MEET WHEN HE ENTERED YOUR LIFE?

_____

_____

_____

_____

3. WHAT THINGS CHANGED IN YOUR LIFE IN THE NEXT FEW DAYS, WEEKS, AND MONTHS?

_____

_____

_____

_____

Now, on a separate sheet of paper, using these questions and answers as a resource, write out your testimony. Don't feel like it has to be perfect. Just write a rough draft, and you can continue working on it with your Paul over a period of time.

Helpful Hints for Writing Out Your Testimony

1. Speak to God first, and ask Him to speak through you. Ask Him to give you wisdom and guidance as you write.

2. Follow a three-point outline:

    a. Life before knowing Christ.

    b. How you came to Christ (be specific).

    c. Life after you received Christ (changes He has made, what He means to you now).

3. Begin with an interesting, attention-getting sentence and close with a good conclusion. Include relevant, thought-provoking, personal experiences.

4. Write in such a way that others will identify with your past and present experiences.

5. Give enough detail to arouse interest.

6. Use some Scripture verses.

7. Avoid —

    a. Using statements which reflect negatively on people or organizations.

    b. Mentioning denominations.

    c. Preaching at people. This is a testimony, not a "preachamony."

    d. Using stereotypes or overworked terms.

    e. Using words or terms that are meaningless to non-Christians, e.g. "salvation," "saved," "born again," "sanctified," etc. If this type of word must be used, it should be clearly explained.

8. Prepare your testimony so that you can share it in a group situation as well as with an individual.

9. Build your testimony around a theme—something characteristic of your life that is of general interest to non-Christians. Examples: personal success (your past vs. present perspective), life goals, etc.

10. Keep in mind that your testimony should give details so that someone else would know how to trust Christ.

11. It is important that Christ be lifted up as the only way to eternal life. Make sure this point is clearly made in your testimony.

12. When you have finished writing your testimony, write one or two names on a "Ten Most Wanted" card of people with whom you would eventually like to share your testimony. Begin praying regularly for those you have listed, that God would:

    a. Prepare their hearts;

    b. Give you sensitivity to them;

    c. Provide an opportunity to share.

II. Why Should I Tell Others?

Ask and Listen Before Telling

In having a desire to share your faith with others, it is very important to get to know them. When you meet with someone, show genuine care by asking questions about them, get to know their heart before sharing your story. Listening intently communicates love. This helps you find areas of common ground and opens up receptivity. If you don't, they may feel as if you're dumping your truckload on them.

WHAT QUESTIONS CAN YOU THINK OF THAT WOULD HELP TO START A SPIRITUAL CONVERSATION?

_____

_____

_____

_____

Be Ready

Perhaps you've heard one of these statements: "Religion is a private matter." "No one should force their interpretation on others." "Believe what you want, but leave me out of it."

SUGGEST A FEW REASONS WHY CHRISTIANS MIGHT BE HESITANT TO SHARE THEIR FAITH.

_____

_____

_____

_____

WHAT ARE THE IMPLICATIONS OF MARK 8:38 FOR US?

_____

_____

_____

_____

In Philemon 6, what is a positive motivator for sharing our faith?

_____

_____

_____

Can't Stop Talking

We share our faith because we are commanded to. It was Jesus' ultimate teaching for us before His ascension. But we also do it out of love, because "salvation is found in no one else"(Acts 4:12). We pass on the news because we want our friends to have the abundant life we have found. But how do we begin?

III. What Should I Say?

Finding the Words

Oh, you'd love to present the gospel; you just need to get around to getting that seminary degree first, right? Actually, the Bible teaches that all Christians can share their faith. It really isn't rocket science.

Read I Peter 3:15, 16. What is Peter's approach to evangelism?

_____

_____

_____

Why are we to have this kind of attitude?

_____

_____

_____

LIKE A GOOD SCOUT, THEN, WE SHOULD "BE PREPARED." YET—ACCORDING TO ACTS 1:8—SOME OF THE PREPARATION HAS ALREADY BEEN ARRANGED. STUDY THAT VERSE AND EXPLAIN WHAT IT SAYS.

_____

_____

_____

_____

The Bottom Line

THE BASIC MESSAGE IS CONTAINED IN ONE SIMPLE VERSE: JOHN 3:16, SOMETIMES CALLED "THE GOSPEL IN A NUTSHELL." USE YOUR OWN WORDS TO REPHRASE AND EXPLAIN THAT VERSE.

_____

_____

_____

_____

PAUL PRESENTED THE GOSPEL EVERYWHERE HE WENT. I CORINTHIANS 15:1-6 ILLUSTRATES HIS SIMPLE EXPLANATION OF THE GOOD NEWS. OUTLINE HIS MAIN POINTS.

_____

_____

_____

_____

That's His Story and I'm Sticking to It

The basic gospel message never changes. God loves us; we fail to live up to His standards; He became a man and claimed our penalty so we could be brought home to Him. But there's another element to your presentation: just as you share His story, you must also share your own real life story. It's called your testimony.

IV. WHO SHOULD I TELL?

So Many People, So Little Time

How many people do you encounter in a day? At work, in restaurants, on planes, at the store—you probably come into contact with more than you think. Just when and with whom can you share the gospel?

THERE IS A WAY TO WITNESS TWENTY-FOUR HOURS A DAY! WHAT IS IT, ACCORDING TO MATTHEW 5:16?

_____

_____

_____

WHAT DOES IT MEAN TO "LET YOUR LIGHT SHINE?" GIVE THE ANSWER FROM I PETER 2:12.

_____

_____

_____

Three Levels of Sharing Our Faith

1. Raising the Flag

2. Faith Stories

3. Testimony

It's important to be sensitive to the moment in sharing Christ with an unbeliever. The Holy Spirit will prod you at the right time and give you the words. But what you say, and how much you share, is affected by such factors as how well and how long you've known your friend, and what your surroundings are at the time. There are times when a hard-hitting, involved testimony can be self-defeating. Here are a couple ways to open doors to share your faith.

1. Raising the Flag:

A flag clearly communicates the allegiance of the one raising it. In casual conversation, it can be easy—and non-threatening—to raise the flag of your faith by mentioning that a prayer has been answered, or that God has been dealing with you recently on an issue. It's also easy to make a reference to a good illustration from the pastor's sermon. These gentle "flags" establish your status as a Christian.

Raising the Flag Principles:

> It should happen as a natural part of a conversation.

> If it takes more than thirty seconds, you're probably saying too much.

> Its purpose is to establish your identity as a member of God's family, not as a member of a religious denomination or affiliation.

2. Faith Stories:

A faith story is a more direct way to talk about the presence of God in your life. While less than a full testimony, it's instead an anecdote about God's love and grace in one specific instance in your life—how He got you through a difficult time, how His blessing came at just the right time. A good, polished faith story will always command attention and open doors.

Faith Story Principles:

> A short story of when a biblical truth made an impact on your life.

> Its purpose is to create hunger in the unbeliever.

Examples:

> Learning something new about business from the Bible.

> Making a decision about work, family or relationships based on the Bible.

3. Testimony:

Paul had many months in prison to prepare his testimony before King Agrippa (Acts 26). The result was a sharp, brief life testimony no one could deny or attack. You'll need to spend some time polishing the story of your conversion. It's one of your most precious tools, so tell it to others.

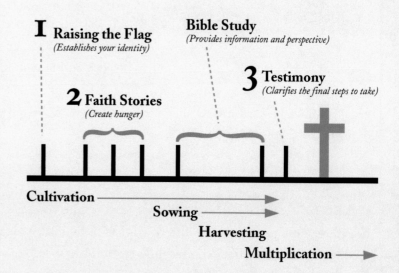

Memory Verse: Telling Others about Christ

I Peter 3:15-16

"But in your hearts set apart Christ as Lord. Always be prepared to give an answer to everyone who asks you to give the reason for the hope that you have. But do this with gentleness and respect, keeping a clear conscience, so that those who speak maliciously against your good behavior in Christ may be ashamed of their slander."

Additional Resources

> www.storyspot.com

> *Living Proof* DVD from CBMC

> *Lifestyle Evangelism*, Joe Aldrich

> *Living Proof*, Jim Petersen

> *Wings of Gold, Wings of Truth*, Fritz Klump

NOTES

[OPTIONAL APPLICATION]

THINK: IF YOU EXPERIENCE THE MIRACLE OF FORGIVENESS AND BEING DEAD AND NOW ALIVE, WHY IS IT SUCH A STRUGGLE TO SHARE IT?

_____

_____

_____

_____

_____

OBSERVE: WATCH *CHARIOTS OF FIRE*. NOTE ERIC LIDDELL'S STORY AS IT UNFOLDS.

_____

_____

_____

_____

_____

CONSIDER: DID YOU ENJOY READING STORIES AS A CHILD? WHAT IS IT ABOUT A STORY THAT SO COMPELS US?

_____

_____

_____

_____

_____

NOTES

NOTES

NEW LIFE IN CHRIST

I JOHN 5:11-13

 And this is the testimony: God has given us eternal life, and this life is in his Son.

He who has the Son has life; he who does not have the Son of God does not have life.

I write these things to you who believe in the name of the Son of God

so that you may know that you have eternal life.

[NIV]

OUR NEW IDENTITY

II CORINTHIANS 5:17

Therefore, if anyone is in Christ,

he is a new creation;

the old has gone, the new has come!

[NIV]

BATTLING THE WORLD, THE FLESH AND THE DEVIL

I PETER 5:8-9

Be self-controlled and alert.

Your enemy the devil prowls around like a roaring lion looking for someone to devour.

Resist him, standing firm in the faith, because you know that your brothers throughout the world are undergoing the same kind of sufferings.

[NIV]

DEALING WITH TEMPTATION

I CORINTHIANS 10:13

No temptation has seized you except what is common to man.

And God is faithful; He will not let you be tempted beyond what you can bear.

But when you are tempted, He will also provide a way out so that you can stand up under it.

[NIV]

DISCOVERING THE HOLY SPIRIT

GALATIONS 5:22-23

 But the fruit of the Spirit is

love, joy, peace, patience,

kindness, goodness, faithfulness,

gentleness and self-control.

Against such things there is no law.

[NIV]

COMMUNICATING WITH GOD

PHILIPIANS 4:6-7

Do not be anxious about anything, but in everything, by prayer and petition, with thanksgiving, present your requests to God.

And the peace of God, which transcends all understanding, will guard your hearts and your minds in Christ Jesus.

[NIV]

TELLING OTHERS OUR STORY

I PETER 3:15-16

 But in your hearts set apart Christ as Lord.

Always be prepared to give an answer to everyone who asks you to give the reason for the hope that you have.

But do this with gentleness and respect, keeping a clear conscience, so that those who speak maliciously against your good behavior in Christ may be ashamed of their slander.

[NIV]

OUR NEW IDENTITY

II CORINTHIANS 5:17

"
Therefore if anyone is in Christ, he is a new creature; the old things passed away; behold, new things have come.
"

[NASB]

NEW LIFE IN CHRIST

I JOHN 5:11-13

And the testimony is this, that God has given us eternal life, and this life is in His Son.

He who has the Son has the life; he who does not have the Son of God does not have the life.

These things I have written to you who believe in the name of the Son of God, so that you may know that you have eternal life.
"

[NASB]

DEALING WITH TEMPTATION

I CORINTHIANS 10:13

"
No temptation has overtaken you but such as is common to man; and God is faithful, who will not allow you to be tempted beyond what you are able, but with the temptation will provide the way of escape also, so that you will be able to endure it.
"

[NASB]

BATTLING THE WORLD, THE FLESH AND THE DEVIL

I PETER 5:8-9

"
Be of sober spirit, be on the alert

Your adversary, the devil, prowls around like a roaring lion, seeking someone to devour.

But resist him, firm in your faith, knowing that the same experiences of suffering are being accomplished by your brethren who are in the world.
"

[NASB]

COMMUNICATING WITH GOD

PHILIPIANS 4:6-7

"
Be anxious for nothing, but in everything by prayer and supplication with thanksgiving let your requests be made known to God.

And the peace of God, which surpasses all comprehension, will guard your hearts and your minds in Christ Jesus.
"

[NASB]

DISCOVERING THE HOLY SPIRIT

GALATIONS 5:22-23

But the fruit of the Spirit is

love, joy, peace, patience,

kindness, goodness, faithfulness,

gentleness, self-control;

against such things there is no law.
"

[NASB]

TELLING OTHERS OUR STORY

I PETER 3:15-16

But sanctify Christ as Lord in your hearts, always being ready to make a defense to everyone who asks you to give an account for the hope that is in you, yet with gentleness and reverence; and keep a good conscience so that in the thing in which you are slandered, those who revile your good behavior in Christ will be put to shame.
"

[NASB]

Made in United States
Orlando, FL
01 March 2024

44281330R00071